Etienne-Jules Marey   A Passion for the Trace

Zone Books • New York • 1992

Translated by Robert Galeta with Jeanine Herman

Etienne-Jules Marey   *A Passion for the Trace*

François Dagognet

Robert Galeta would like very much to thank Martin Joughin and Raymond Rushforth and especially Anne-Marie Cervera, Jane Shaw and the students of the Veterinary School of Lyon.

Originally published in France as *Etienne-Jules Marey: La Passion de la trace*, © 1987 by Editions Hazan.

Printed in the United States of America.

Distributed by The MIT Press,
Cambridge, Massachusetts, and London, England

Library of Congress Cataloging in Publication Data

Dagognet, François.
    Etienne-Jules Marey : a passion for the trace /
François Dagognet.
        p. cm.
    Includes bibliographical references and index.
    ISBN 0-942299-64-7 — ISBN 0-942299-65-5 (paper)
    1. Marey, Etienne-Jules, 1830–1904. 2. Chronophotography.
I. Title.
TR849.M37D33   1992
770'.92–DC20   92-22139
                                                CIP

Contents

Foreword

This book aims to present the main features of the work of Etienne-Jules Marey and to elucidate his methodology as well as his philosophy as a scientist. A few words are needed, however, by way of a prologue, about Marey himself, as his life is something of an enigma. Only particularly striking or odd aspects of Marey's life will be mentioned here, along with anything that provides a better approach to the scientific work itself.

Marey was born in Beaune (Côte d'Or) on March 5, 1830, and from the outset was an intriguing man. At birth he was registered with only the first name Etienne, and was baptized on May 2 as Jules-Etienne. His parents and friends called him "Jules," as would the plaque on the street named after him in Beaune: "Rue Jules-Marey, Physiologist, 1830–1904." When Marey later went to live in Paris, he always used the signature "E. J. Marey" or, on rare occasions, "Etienne." Marey the scientist seems to separate himself from the Marey whose origins were in Burgundy.

The young Jules Marey, only child of the bookkeeper Claude Marey (today he would be called a "manager" or "sales manager") of Bouchard wines of Beaune, received a careful, religious education. It was his mother's fervent wish that he become a priest. He himself wanted to be an engineer; this desire can be seen in the "Mr. Punch robot" he made as a child with his lifelong friend Julien Bouchard (the son of his father's employers). His father's advice was to triumph in the end: he dreamed of the Beaune hospital for his son and thus pointed him in the direction of medicine.

The son who had always shown true and loyal affection for his parents, as their letters reveal, was a rapid and dazzling success. First in his class of student residents at the Paris Hospital (in 1854), his medical thesis later won immediate notice in the highest circles: at 39 he succeeded Pierre Flourens at the Collège de France.

His ordination was complete but it is striking that he nonetheless returned, by way of biology, to his first inclinations: engineering, invention and mechanism. Out of the field of medicine that was advocated for him, he was to become the physicist that he wanted to be.

In 1870 he bought a villa near Naples. Recluse that he was, Marey stayed there for part of the winter, spending the rest of the year in Paris or Beaune; more precisely, from 1874, in the Domaine de la Folie, near Chagny. This Italian exile cannot be ignored; it was to mark his work as his work would mark its period.

In Paris, where (after 1870) he would reside from spring until autumn, Marey often changed residence: rue Cuvier, then rue de l'Ancienne Comédie and, finally, 11 boulevard Delessert. In his various apartments, filled with homemade machines and appliances, including a merry-go-round, visitors were struck by the "science bazaar" in which the scientist lived. He spoke of himself as a "physiologist working at home," "curio-hunter" and "medical engineer." Jean-Baptiste Chauveau wrote, "Who, in the world of physiology of the time, French or foreign, did not know of this curious and picturesque equipment?" In fact, boulevard Delessert was where he was finally able to put an end to this cumbersome life because he found himself close to the Physiological Station in the Parc des Princes where he could devote himself unhindered to his experiments.

His situation was not unusual. Scientists in the nineteenth century often had to set up their own school, equip their laboratory and work independently of any institution, even if they became part of one at a later date. Marey did not escape this rule of "comparatively amateurish beginnings."

Was his life dedicated solely to disinterested scientific research? Was it his only passion? His biographer has been neither able nor willing to say; his existence remains impenetrable: "There is a totally unknown life of Marey, the thread of which I have been able to guess through certain confidences I have caught. This private life which Marey adamantly concealed shall not be entered into.... Marey had to deal with many problems, jealousies and accusations," writes Henri Savonnet. I shall leave the subject there, except to note that in his will (he died on May 15, 1904) Marey requested cremation and a civil funeral.

Moreover, it is not necessary to know about his life to understand his work. I have nonetheless tried to underline the constant dual track that it followed: two distinct first names indicating him; two homes between which he divided his time, Italy in winter and France (Paris and Beaune) in summer; and two workplaces – an interior scientific or biological space that quickly overflowed the laboratory walls to incorporate the flight of birds in the air, the racing of horses on the track and, above all, the lapping of waves on the beach. His apartment was certainly transformed into a laboratory, but he worked just as much outside in nature itself, where he was intent on recording the swiftest of movements.

If his work is likewise steeped in the same regular and thorough ambivalence or duality, it also leads from one surprise to the next: logical, yet metamorphosing as it went along, its development would remain distinctly unforeseeable.

1. Etienne-Jules Marey photographed by
   Nadar, around 1870–1875.

Preface

Marey, a physician, or more precisely a physiologist, had a revolutionary effect on medicine, art, technology and culture. But why and how? It was not the first time that a clinician or scientist had interested himself in the creative arts. But others generally would do so only to decipher a body of work (monograph) or to discover the individual roots of a given innovation.

In Marey's case we have not a discrete relationship between science and art but something on the way to their fusion. My aim is to make the symbiosis clearer.

Marey first studied – and thus had to transcribe – the motions of the organs (heart rhythms, muscle tremors, lung ventilation). He then went on to animal locomotion: the bird's flight, the horse's gallop, the insect's quiver. He would take this to its ultimate conclusion: kinetics of isolated flows, eddies in air, ripples in water and wave patterns.

At the same time he was constantly replacing crude "recorders" with more sensitive ones; mechanical would be superseded by electrical and then chemical recording (the chronophotographic gun [figure 2], the partial photography of an animal or man reduced to a line, moving film stock and so on). A world now arose that could not be grasped by looking. He simplified, halted and merged; things were made uniform and blurred. The tumultuous, abrupt and multiple would be unleashed on all sides by his instruments.

We may have had the idea that "motion" was continuous and gradual, but our retinal apparatus was deceiving us. It is the latter that blends together or dissolves. The universe is made up in reality of surges and drops, ruptures that we synthesize and so diminish. It is we who construct a continuous, rounded scene. Mareyism would shatter an illusion that was being strengthened by the philosophy of Bergson. Marey's activity would have an impact on art, for the futurists as well as the cubists. It would henceforth be possible to express speed, or at least movement, more powerfully.

A further potential came into being. The scientist could capture diverse phases of motion, dismantle them and, in consequence, reassemble them (cinematographic illusionism). Because they had been apprehended, they also could be restored (cinematics).

Projecting devices far superior to Joseph Plateau's phenakistoscope, Emile Raynaud's praxinoscope or Thomas Edison's kinetoscope would be perfected; nothing would stop the rise of techniques for obtaining recordings. The voice (phonautography) would be changed into tracings and microgrooves; having been recorded it was sure to be reproduced. Restoring image and sound would even become a simultaneous operation: the birth of the culture industry.

More than simply providing it with a set of instruments, Mareyism unveiled another universe that the culture industry was invited to take up. Why stop at academic immobility or even kinetic melody when one could uncover a world of tensions, phases and fluctuations? Let us save the image from torpor!

The living world is filled with jolts, rustlings, rhythms and continual tremors. In bringing to light muscle stimulation or the forcing power of the cardiac pump ceaselessly beating, Mareyism offered a distinctly dynamic image of life.

By the same token, he gave life to images, which henceforth flew like birds. At the same time, he promoted the construction of devices or speed vehicles (the airplane) and hastened the reign of speed; life and speed, then, would be complemented by an art that vibrated and flashed.

2. Male nude posing in Albert Londe's chronophotographic laboratory at Salpêtrière. Marey is seated at the extreme right of the picture.

3. Picture of a bird in flight obtained using
the first photographic gun, 1882.

Early Principles

I insist on Marey's importance for three main reasons:

1. No one was as successful at making visible what kept to the shadows. How were these dark areas to be lighted? The forces of life are hidden; by transposing them he brought them fully into the light.

2. From this, Marey would try to go further and track down the imperceptible, the fleeting, the tumultuous and the flashing. The extraordinary "image-maker" would demonstrate how one could tame what was elusive (figure 3).

3. He would gradually point researchers toward a different understanding of the relations between science and art, between the real and figuration which he would liberate. Marey's thinking constantly expanded; its beginnings must be duly considered.

The author's earliest works date from the year 1854 (according to his *Notice sur les titres et travaux scientifiques* compiled in 1868), the same year as his successful entry into the Paris Hospital as an intern. His medical doctorate, defended March 4, 1859, was entitled *Recherches sur la circulation du sang à l'état sain et dans les maladies.*

This thesis was preceded, and more importantly followed, by a cluster of articles that completed and clarified it, published in the *Journal de l'Anatomie et de la Physiologie,* the *Gazette Médicale de Paris,* the *Journal de Physiologie de l'Homme et des Animaux,* the *Annales de Sciences Naturelles,* the *Archives Générales de Médecine* and the *Comptes Rendus de l'Académie des Sciences,* among others.

What were Marey's general theses at this early stage? First, he consistently restated his mechanist and antivitalist beliefs against those who obscured the phenomena of health and illness and who refused to explain or even describe them fully. In one of his earliest works, he clearly stated this:

> The prime cause of movement in the living being seems to be of a special order, without parallel in inanimate bodies, but once movement is produced it is the same, whatever its source.... It is the difficulty of clearly determining their nature which has led to classifying them prematurely among vital phenomena, thus distracting from their study and halting progress completely, often for a long time.[1]

Not long after, in *Animal Mechanism: A Treatise on Terrestrial and Aerial Locomotion*, published in 1873, he again criticized this attitude. The identification of life forms with machines had not been properly thought out and, hence, poorly put into practice. One spoke of a jumble of pulleys, ropes, levers, valves and pumps, but "these passive organs need a motor. It is life, it was said, that, in animals, set all these mechanisms going, and it was therefore believed that an inviolable barrier between inanimate and animate machines could be established."[2] Marey, however, goes on: "modern engineers have created machines that can be much more legitimately compared to animated motors. These, by means of the fuel they consume, supply the force requisite to animate a series of organs, and to make them execute the most diverse operations."[3]

This declaration of mechanist belief, however, did not lead to oversimplification, or the usual "reductionism." On the contrary, the sole concern was to catch life at its most characteristic: its incessant movement (the moving image). We sought its "signature," so that it would surrender its rhythms and variations in the form of graphic lines.

Because traditional methods could not be employed, two problems had to be contended with straightaway. First, experiments involving bleeding could not be performed on humans, only on animals. Only in the latter could a nerve be bared and cut, an organ removed or, a slightly less vivisectionist process, a glandular duct be diverted outside (fistula). However, absolute limits would soon present themselves and, in any case, such removals and excisions gave rather suspect results. An authentic physiological approach, which one hoped could enter into the very play of the forces of life, could not be initiated by a process of destruction. Discontinuing and interrupting, then, seemed neither appropriate nor sufficient.

Second, if one was limited to taking observations of signs and developments in humans and animals, one would end up with merely an unrevealing blur of phenomena. The truth about a given function or its pathological disorder would be elusive. Marey was able to dismiss the observation of indicators and symptoms. Sight, hearing and touch did not present him with the really noteworthy features; their capacity was limited. It is true that the doctor at the patient's bedside observed the general aspect, the facies, and that he collected a great deal of information: the occurrence of either swelling or depletion, or a panting breath, for instance. Marey maintained that, not only do the senses often conceal the essential, they also lead to mistakes. The introduction to his *La Méthode graphique* warned that:

the spherical nature of the earth, its daily rotation, the distances of the stars and their immense volumes, all our knowledge of astronomy, so to speak, contradicts the appraisal of our senses. The same can be said about a whole host of notions in physics and mechanics, such as the heaviness of air, the discontinuity of sounds and light, and so forth. The sensations of coldness and heat that our sense of touch provides no longer have the absolute meaning they were once given.[4]

Sight in particular is locked within a circle from which it cannot escape, even though the telescope and microscope have greatly enlarged its circumference. Hearing and touch delude even more, although psychological analysis of their shortcomings has not gone as far as in the case of sight.

Thus, Marey clearly distanced himself from the clinician who was overinclined to collect and rely on whatever symptoms appeared: the hand feeling a certain tremor, and the ear following murmurs and noises (mostly cardiopulmonary). With the help of his stethoscope, René Laennec learned to hear and interpret these, but Marey, from his earliest writings, qualified his approach. What is more complex than a movement? It was necessary to know "the amplitude, force, duration, regularity, and shape. And if the force of this movement is not enough for us to be able to perceive it, if its duration is too short for us to have the time to analyze the other features. . . ."[5] Neither direct, violent experimentation nor observation would be enough. To repeat my point, Marey would have to invent other means.

Moreover, the organism was wrapped in a number of different layers, inevitable superimpositions and invaginations that hid growths and muffled noises. The body veiled itself. It was necessary to go beyond symptomatology: "The symptoms given by sounding are suspect: the moving heart prevents our determining the exact origin of the noises."[6] Marey's argument is a little surprising, but it shows to what extent he sought less apparent kinds of evidence and proof.

But even supposing a minuscule, indeed pathognomonic, hypothetically conclusive symptom could be observed, it could not be retained, let alone transmitted, due to its fleeting nature:

If a doctor gifted with a subtle sense of touch and great patience manages, through observation, to recognize important features in the pulse of certain patients, how will he explain to his students what he himself senses? Will he find in them a sense of touch naturally delicate enough to discern immediately sensations that he himself could only distinguish after much effort? Will he hope to explain the nature of tactile sensation through definitions or metaphors?[7]

Marey was consistent: he refused everything that came through sensation. In fact, one could borrow the phrase *testis unus, testis nullus.*

He rejected, then, both experiment and observation. To get out of this methodological impasse, the clinician resorted to exploratory instruments: endoscopes that made it possible to see inside hollow organs that were lit up, as in the laryngoscope; or probes that extended the fingers, pushing back the limitations of touch, which went down into the stomach, for example, to indicate the absence of stricture in a duct. There was Pierre Piorry's pleximeter (1828), intended to replace direct manual sounding: a fine, hard, yet supple metal plate, or, on occasion, an ivory plate, was applied to some area of the body and struck by a hammer, which had a rubber pad fitted to its head. Soft hands had been definitively replaced; here was on one side a firm surface and on the other a sharp striking force able to reveal the cavities beneath (tympanism). The aim was to improve and widen Leopold Auenbrugger's method, taken up by Jean Nicolas Corvisart:

> While direct sounding practiced on many of the abdominal areas produces little or no sound, mediate sounding of this cavity gives a quite remarkable noise throughout. This advantage results from the pleximeter adding a kind of solid wall to the soft casings of the abdomen.... Each organ studied by the pleximeter has a special sound (jecoral, humoric, osteal, etc.).[8]

Curiously, the poverty of the results would be accompanied by a lexical lavishness, a whole recasting of nomenclature (pleximetrism, inseparable from its onomatopathology, as in aeroperitonasia, epidiaphratopy, cholihepatasia and so on). Marey's criticism, however, did not change: this method, like the others (Laennec's stethoscopics), only extended the senses, while what was needed was to disown them. One should not contemplate improving them; they did not play a "revealing" role. For disturbance sometimes affected, not simply a diffuse function, but one of its components. It was therefore necessary to separate the information and assessments. This was precisely why traditional instruments were no longer appropriate, including the manometer, which gave the overall facts or resultant, but not the various factors competing with or neutralizing one another. From the outset, Marey stressed not only the importance of what he called "local circulations," but also the imbrication of forces — that of the heart muscle, that of the vessels — as well as the contraction or relaxation of the capillaries. It was important to distinguish between them, but how? The classic instruments were unable to discriminate between the signals they picked up.

Without knowing it, the doctor's role ultimately was that of a screen: distorting, slowing down and omitting. When he or she intervened, only general phenomena could be grasped; thus, the doctor had to be replaced. This meant putting aside once and for all his or her own receiving devices of sight, touch and hearing, and inventing processes of direct inscription, so as to separate life from its secrets, put it in the open and force a "direct writing" from it (graphy).

Abruptly, in the mid-nineteenth century, Marey's physiopathology unceremoniously made obsolete a number of trends: Laennec's symptomatology and its tools, making great progress at the time; the Morgan approach (lesion research, so-called anatomical sighting); and physiological experiments on animals (vivisection). Marey set out on his own path; one that, in my view, revolutionized biology and its methods.

———————————

The success of visibility, far in advance of the results of less adequate sensory recordings, did not come about all of a sudden. It was inspired by earlier work that I have to consider to understand fully Marey's contribution.

I thus begin a long and difficult examination, with four main strands to guide me toward a conclusion. One should not forget the reward at the end of the analysis; it includes some unexpected fireworks – the premises of the modern world, the transformation of art, communication and society. Who would have imagined that a modest problem in biology would have so many indirect consequences? I recall one of my central tenets here: that the image of life that Marey was to bring out of the shadows would immediately, and inevitably, give life to images (art) and suddenly free them from their inertia. Industry would be overwhelmingly affected as well.

In the early nineteenth century, physiology was quite properly concerned with the "cardiac muscle," impressive both for its energy (*primum movens, ultimum moriens*) and its remarkable capacity to work automatically. Marey went straight to the center of the debate but, at the same time, began to develop an interest in "arterial contractility." This was not simply because his physiology was already turning away from general considerations, but specifically because the vessels apparently modified or even controlled the workings of the heart. This "second peripheral heart" seemed to overshadow the first: "creating either local or general resistances in the path of this single motor, it [contraction] stems the passage of blood to a greater or lesser extent, whether in a specific point in the body or in the system as a whole."[9] Thus, in the wake of Claude Bernard, who had described vaso-motivity, Marey participated in the slight shift of subject and examination toward the circulatory system. It was the occasion for one of Marey's first accomplishments, and one very much in character. If it was impossible to capture life's movements, then a mechanical "model" would have to be constructed to work from. Such a machine was thus made. It

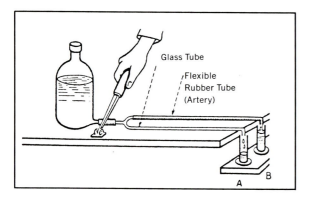

Glass Tube

Flexible
Rubber Tube
(Artery)

A   B

4. Diagram of one of Marey's experiments on blood flow. In B, the flow is
continuous and the output greater than in A.

had the benefit of being made in a period in which there was great success at assembling ingenious devices: there was Claude Chappe and his aerial telegraph; and Louis Bréguet and his son, the clockmakers. The former gave us sensitive meters, bell springs, chiming clocks and musical boxes; the latter a host of different devices: a chronograph, a seismograph, a photophone and so on. There was also Marcel Deprez, the physicist who, in addition to a galvanometer named jointly after him and Jacques d'Arsonval, invented a manometer for measuring variable pressure.[10] In this case, the entire arterial tree was simulated and boldly experimented with, which revealed precisely the importance of wall elasticity in the flow of blood (figure 4).

A container full of water, a Mariotte bottle, was placed on a stand with two tubes, one glass and one flexible rubber, leading from it. The tap at the base was alternately opened and closed, or a clamp was tightened or slackened to simulate the jolts of the intermittent heart pump. The inert, rigid channel (of glass) gave an irregular and also less plentiful supply than the flexible one. The rubber channel's elasticity made the motor's work more economical. This mimetic experiment suggested that the artery played a decisive role in irrigating the body. The tubes were most important: they were not passive transporters of blood, they assisted and amplified the flow (figure 4).

Marey's physiology consisted of making use of equivalent schemas and then going beyond them to reach complex and elusive organic processes. However, two problems occupied it: First, what were the movements in question and how were they linked? The task could not be undertaken by the senses:

> The time taken for one turn of the heart was so short that it prevented us from catching the succeeding phenomena occurring in the space of a second. When one has seen unprejudiced men, long used to physiological experiments, observing a bared heart and disagreeing over the order of the successive movements, one has to admit that the eye is not suitable for catching these complex movements that follow each other so rapidly....[11]

This is a constant motif: circulations are either much too fast or extremely slow and, hence, elude us.

Second, even if movements could be grasped, examining them was complicated. Their force, speed, rhythm, amplitude, supply and so on all had to be known: What happened specifically in the vessels and how could one evaluate what unfolded on the inside from the outside? The question might equally be posed like this: Given that we find ourselves on the periphery, how can we gain a precise understanding of the artery and measure everything happening in it without having to penetrate it? How could we realize teledetection?

To get out of this dilemma, Marey would at some point leave biology behind to find useful tricks, which he would later apply to it (transfer of research). He would invent recording processes. Let me also note that there was no great upheaval; he took a result and extended and shifted its limits. He made gains by this widening of frontiers, although he never took full advantage of it. He was already meticulous and subtle, an analyst of genius, even if he was constrained by these very qualities and held back by a kind of reserve. However, there was a surprise in store. The man who restricted himself to apparently minor problems and avoided all excess, would nonetheless, unbeknown to himself, take part in the beginnings of a cultural upheaval: first in how we look at things, then in our surroundings and our factories.

Let me begin the long analysis of what made this mutation come about. For the first of the four strands to be considered, I turn to the great work of Jean-Baptiste Chauveau, head of anatomical research at the Veterinary School of Lyon. From 1861, Marey was his associate (they published jointly), so similar were their approaches to arterio- and cardiography.

    With Chauveau, the questions began to shift somewhat, even though he still used methods that would soon be outmoded. Until this time, the detection of vital phenomena, particularly of the heart, had been carried out on humans, especially on a subject whose unusual condition made examination easier. Thus Doctor Upham of Boston tried to trace the movements of the heart, auricles and ventricles in a young doctor named Groux, who suffered from a congenital division of the sternum "in whom the heartbeats could be felt very near the surface." For lack of such an exceptional case, the physiologist would experiment in the laboratory on reptiles, frogs and also fish (the eel), which were suitable because "the heart can be exposed without affecting the workings of their respiratory organs."[12] It was preferable if the animals were small, but there was a price to be paid for the advantages: while performing thoracic openings on them was easy, their heart movements were so fast that it was impossible to take in all the stages. Mistakes were made. But, in his veterinary school, where he dissected adult and old horses for teaching purposes, Chauveau made discoveries difficult to come by in other circumstances, with three main advantages facilitating progress: (1) a horse's heartbeat was strong but also slow, measuring thirty-five beats per minute against seventy in humans; (2) its myocardium presented a relatively spacious cavity that was easy to explore, with probes being introduced into the ventricles and the carotid artery itself; and (3) the finger could be inserted without fear of causing a heart attack, so that the workings of the valves could be sampled, particularly inside the auriculoventricular passage: "When the ventricles begin contracting, one can feel the tricuspid valves straightening again."[13] The blood was prevented from flowing backward! The chronology of the phases was thus assured and, as Chauveau noted, the physiologists' novel (the heart laid bare) could be replaced by a natural history.

Thanks to his "study material" and his procedures, including direct sensory examination (palpation), Chauveau shed light on the mechanism of heart cycles. Moreover, he was beginning to turn a corner; there was a shift from direct to mediate physiology, because the noises of the heart alone would tell us how it was working. Collecting them was not enough: we had to grasp the information they possessed.

Their interpretation had given rise to explanations that the Lyon physiologist was to sweep aside. He proposed the concept of the valvular origin of heart sounds: the first noise (systolic) corresponded to the closing of the mitral and tricuspid (the auriculoventriculars); and the second was the blood hitting the buffer of the aortic sigmoids, which stopped it from flowing back again. Chauveau presented irrefutable evidence that invalidated the rather naive thesis that had the heart banging against the thoracic wall, like a visitor knocking at the door. François Magendie, in 1835, was vigorously defending this hypothesis:

Is it not, moreover, on this sonority of the thoracic walls that the whole theory of percussion is based? When your finger knocks on the chest you get a sound; similarly when the heart comes and strikes this same chest you should likewise hear a sound. I see no difference between these two kinds of percussion.... What does it matter if it is against the inside or the outside surface of the pectoral wall that the shock is produced...?[14]

Magendie thought he had reliable evidence: if the sternum were removed, or if a layer of tow were placed between the heart and this bony plate, the noise stopped. Chauveau, however, spoiled the story, just as he largely ignored the excessive importance given to agitation of liquids, collisions and friction of the blood against the endocardium. He inserted a finger into the valve to stop its full closure, causing the thumping to grow immediately faint. Correlatively, Chauveau explained abnormal beating by the blood having to pass through a reduced gap (mitral stenosis). In short, he provided a firm foundation for valve theory, or phonocardiography. He finally shed light on the stronghold of vitality (the noises of the myocardium).

In the case of the arteries, he would invent a measuring instrument called the haemodromometer (without knowing it, if he is to be believed):

I needed a new device. One day, I had the idea of sticking a needle into the carotid of a horse that had been opened up for an experiment on the scarring of arterial wounds. The needle had been introduced at right angles to the vessel's axis and extended about six or seven millimeters inside it. I had nearly let go of it when I saw it making a quite regular oscillation according to the movement of the blood circulating in the vessel, deviating a great deal when the blood was moving quickly, and straightening up, because of the elasticity of the artery walls, when circulation was halted.[15]

The principle of the instrument was forged. It now needed (1) a hollow metal tube a few centimeters long, and the same in diameter, to act as part of a vessel, and a needle attached to it whose movement across a graduated dial would give the exact speed of the blood; and (2) a microblade to fit the lower tip of the needle to drive it properly. The instrument was set up on the horse's carotid artery, which was easy to get at. As soon as it was cut, the tube was stuck into the two ends and held by ligatures. The operation came up against a number of problems: the tiniest air pocket, for example, could produce clotting and had to be eliminated. According to Chauveau, the speed would reach 50 cm per second. Probing the heart with a strong, slow rhythm, inventing the haemodromometer, and using the nature and location of his work to advantage, Chauveau animated cardio- and arteriography. It is understandable that Marey, the graphic specialist, should want to work with him; together they would continue the work of recording and assessing.

Marey would gradually be able to improve "the sensors." He entered a field of his own, finding sampling methods as sensitive as they were nonviolent. How could he measure the force of the myocardium or the speed of the blood precisely and without effraction? How could he examine the fleeting and rapid? Or, to use an earlier phrase, how could he make the invisible visible? The German school of physiology, which also concentrated on haemodromometric problems, would become as important to Marey's development as Chauveau had been.

The German physiologists had perfected a number of instruments for measuring, for instance, the speed of the blood in its channels and the tension within the arteries that modifies the flow. These techniques would inspire Marey. Why the superiority of the German school? Reading Johannes Müller, one of its founders, in his famous *Handbuch des Physiologie des Menschen* (1838), suggests an answer. Hegel's former pupil was convinced of the fundamental importance of vitality, the harmonious whole (the idea realized, one might say). He wrote:

Each part has its cause, not in itself, but in the cause of the whole.... It is highly unlikely that the vital principle which produces all the parts of an organism according to one idea or one type should itself be made of parts.... A thing that is by nature made up of parts changes its nature when it comes to be divided.[16]

Ingenious methods would provide access to this living substance, and a certain, relative "decomposition" or analysis would foster genuine understanding of this "whole" (the use, for example, of comparative anatomy). The complexity of the organic, then, was no bar to the use of ways and "means" or methods; on the contrary, those who were too ready to simplify risked bothering too little with the discriminating procedures of examination. Physicalism might turn out to be even less appropriate than adherence to Romantic philosophies. I note, moreover, that Müller specialized in problems relating to energy and that he also highlighted the most psychophysiological questions – particularly sight – and that he even supported the theory that a sensation is a creation of the nerve itself.

The will to capture the hidden and most turbulent forces resulted in three new devices from his pupils. Each of these data-collecting devices must be looked at because one of Marey's first inventions attempted to improve and go beyond them. He thus imported physiological devices from Müller's school into France, and this eventually made a considerable impact.

In 1850, Alfred Volkmann constructed a piezometer (*piesein*, "to squeeze," and *metron*, "a measure," thus a kind of manometer or pressure gauge) more advanced than Jean-Louis Poiseuille's (*Recherches sur la force du coeur aortique*, 1828). Poiseuille simply cut the artery, tied one end in a ligature and inserted into the other the lip of a tube leading to a container of mercury whose rise he measured. The method was not only crude but contradictory: in sectioning a vessel, he halted the circulation that he intended to "evaluate." Not surprisingly, the results he obtained were wrong.

Volkmann did better by taking a fine, metal, T-shaped tube and inserting it into the two ends of the momentarily cut vessel, while the perpendicular part was linked to a double column of mercury. With this device, the blood continued to flow and the heart to beat. But the results from this elementary instrument also were questionable. Being inert, the mercury would either increase or decrease the oscillations of arterial pressure. Moreover, only the "jolts" registered, the maximum and minimum produced by the cardiac pump.

This last disadvantage, at least, would be overcome with Karl Ludwig's kymograph (*kūma*, "swell," "wave"). He placed a very light float on the meniscus of the mercury. On it was mounted a slender vertical stem tapering to a point, which traced the variations on a cylinder moving at constant speed perpendicular to the needle's shifts.

This was a great improvement. The curve could be retained and considered as continuous evidence. Direct reading, which only showed divergences, could now be dispensed with. The amplitude of oscillation (the intensity of force), as well as its frequency, could now be recorded. Marey's wishes were answered: the transfer onto paper allowed objective, verifiable examination as well as exact measurement. However, fundamental objections remained. Mercury was still being used, giving deceptive results. This is why Marey and Chauveau first thought of replacing this heavy medium with air, which had little mass and was not inert (simply using thin rubber bulbs to receive the blood pressure passed to them directly by a noncoagulant liquid).

However, in 1855, Karl von Vierordt invented a different method, allowing physiology to avoid bloody incision (mutilation) because it was based on "the pulse." Earlier medicine had concentrated on pulse, but with such poor means of measurement that the practice had fallen into disuse.

Insofar as unreliable palpation was still being used, it deserved to disappear. Hérisson had, in fact, invented a "sphygmometer" (*sphygmos*, "pulse"), which translated tactile into visual data, but the point was not to convert one form of sensory information into another, but to dispense with all of them.

Vierordt's sphygmometer squeezed the artery slightly by pressing a lever against it. Its release was then registered by an ultralight pencil marking on the lamp-black of a revolving cylinder. The two main obstacles to correct assessment had thus disappeared: (1) the sectioned artery, because the pulse sufficed; and (2) both the mercury medium and air were replaced by a thin steel stem, which marked out its own movement.

All Marey had to do was to incorporate these developments in a more sensitive device, for the results that appeared in Vierordt's tables were still questionable.

Marey – adept at detecting revealing vibrations – would not entertain clearly inadequate sphygmometric data. He equipped himself with an instrument that allowed him to understand circulation properly, in terms of both the factors at work and their potential pathological disorder. It was he who would follow up on and yet relegate to the past the manometer, piezometer, kymograph and Vierordt's sphygmometer, while continuing to perfect his system of recording.

Marey's brilliance lay in the discovery of how to make recordings without recourse to the human hand or eye. Nature had to testify to itself, to translate itself through the inflection of curves and subtle trajectories that were truly representative. Hidden, minute and fleeting, life's movements had to be captured (life is movement and nothing else). Chauveau and the German school had helped to put Marey on the right track, but physicists also would supply him with a few tricks. In the material sciences, one learned how to measure tension (force), displacement, and duration; in other words, speed (chronometry). The natural sciences would be a blueprint for biology.

Throughout his writings, Marey refers to the history of notation. Three of his observations in particular would inform his work: First, the most consistent reference is to a machine by Arthur Morin and Jean Poncelet.[17] A falling body described the curve of its fall. A stylus then brushed against a revolving cylinder coated with black. The important thing was that this was "a continuous indication." When the paper was unrolled, a parabola appeared as a result of the combination of two movements, one accelerating, the other constant. Taking the reading seemed less important than the act of recording it. For Marey, it was the ability to transfer that counted, after which conclusions could be drawn with relative ease.

If the cylinder alone turned, without the mass that held the stylus falling, the latter would merely trace a circle, in other words a straight line. But if the mass dropped while the recording cylinder remained at rest, a vertical line appeared. By putting together the rotation of one and the falling of the other, a line was formed between the horizontal and the vertical. The fact that it was a curve was in itself evidence of the nonuniformity of the movement. Two constants added together would only generate a straight line with a certain slope. One could go further. Initially, the tracing hugged the horizontal, but at the end of its travel it moved close to the vertical, showing the predominance of the falling over the rotating movement. Because the rotation of the cylinder was constant, it was clearly not its movement that accelerated but that of the body. Thus, from a recording alone, from a graph, the nature of the variation and the energies involved could be inferred; only the final formula could better the reading. The traced intermediary was not only a way of materializing the phenomenon and getting to its essentials, it facilitated an understanding of it.

Second, another device equally suggestive to Marey was James Watt's diagram based closely on the workings and cycle of the steam engine. Here again, a revolving cylinder, connected to a piston, allowed the recording of variations in pressure. An amplifying lever OAM, moveable at O, was activated by a piston P in equilibrium with the force exerted to the lower part and a spring situated on its upper surface (figure 5). The movement of M was

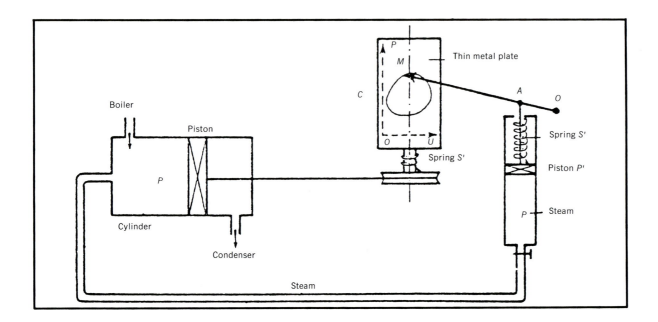

5. Watt's diagram.

proportionate to the variable, that is, the pressure received. In addition, through an arrangement of taut wire and a pulley, the cylinder turned in conjunction with the movement of the fire-powered machine. In essence, two pistons and two springs: This manograph not only illustrated the work brought about due to heat, but also enabled it to be calculated.[18]

Third, another innovation was Thomas Young's cylinder axis, which moved in a simple spiral. With this modification, the inscription could go on longer without danger of superimposing, and thus store more information. Young also must be credited with a "complementary" or extra discovery: "When a stem fitted with a stylus vibrates as it rubs against the surface of a revolving cylinder, it traces a wavy line, each undulation of which corresponds to a vibration of the stem. The time which elapses between the registering of two consecutive vibrations is always the same, since these vibrations are isochronic...."[19] The way to chronography was thereby opened (the stem would later be replaced by a tuning fork).

Marey lists numerous applications and illustrations, particularly in his book *La méthode graphique*. This type of test became widely used, principally in meteorology and geology. Bréguet doubtless alerted him to the variety and potential of all these recording devices. He had invented several himself, notably the udometer (or pluviometer), which he installed in the observatory at Montsouris (a float on a tank collecting water; a moveable needle able to translate the rises in level; the result, a curve on a revolving cylinder).

Marey now turned primarily to engineers for help with improving readings. The problem was that the movement to be transposed either went far beyond the edge of the paper or was so small that it eluded the instruments' graphic capacity. Both cases meant failure. How could one reduce the enormous or, conversely, enlarge the minute?

Marey learned how to overcome this predicament and change scale, with the help of systems of levers and cogs as well as some simpler procedures. Imagine a piece of wire fixed at the top O while its lower end is free to move. Instead of the oscillations of A, let us take those of B. If this is in the middle, its movement, isochronic with A's, will be half of A's. B may be moved closer to O, thus enabling the movement to be reduced without modifying its speed. It is essential to reduce the extent of the curve (figures 6a, 6b).

Conversely, one can increase it: only a simple moveable lever on a fulcrum is needed (the shorter traverse BA will be multiplied by its homologue AO) (figure 6b). The operation is facilitated by using a system of gears: one cog wheel engages a second, which either reduces or amplifies the play of movement (the manometer with a humped surface) (figure 7). This still did not solve the problem, however. It, in effect, reappeared in the inscription of complex movements (multiple or simultaneous movements, that is: one phenomenon in

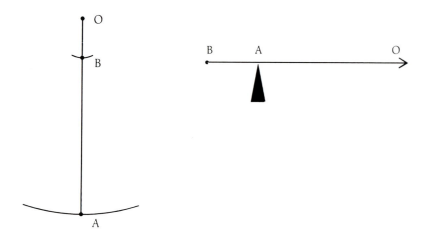

6a, 6b. Oscillation diagrams.

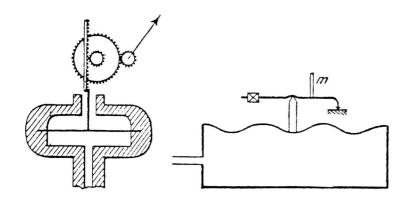

7. Diagram of a manometer with a distorting membrane,
    inspired by Marey.

various places or several phenomena in the same place), or even a single movement that was neither small nor large but of long duration (a prolonged one, hence "the black box" of fast vehicles like the railway locomotive). "We should have to use," wrote Marey, "a sheet of paper a meter square to record the progress of a moving body for twenty kilometers. And this immense surface would only bear the inscription of a single fine line dividing it diagonally into two parts."[20] Marey thus proposed fragmenting the trace so as to keep it on a single narrow band that would retain the essentials (figure 8). The inscription not only secured and trapped the real, it collected and compressed it with no loss of information.

Marey would subsequently abandon these stratagems and devices upon the appearance of two revolutionary possibilities that offered more reliable and sophisticated data collection.

The unresponsiveness of the early devices and, hence, poor transfer and loss of information led to the use of electricity. A quicker, livelier pen could only be an advantage:

> This is how [Paul] Regnard's device is set up. Above the column in a thermometer a metal point is fixed to the writing stylus and moves with it; as soon as this point touches the mercury, it completes an electric current. By virtue of this current, an electromagnet activates a wheel which lifts the stylus and causes the point to leave the mercury. The current thus interrupted sets going a wheel turning in the opposite direction, bringing the point back in contact with the mercury. . . . [21]

Thus heavy floats and levers were replaced by a "medium" that could pass on transformations and slight oscillations more rapidly and sensitively. (Later still, photography would offer more direct and sensitive snapshots.)

It was in the sensitivity and ingeniousness of the "sensor" that the answers still lay. I stress, and shall return to, the great contributions of physicists and inventors to Marey's

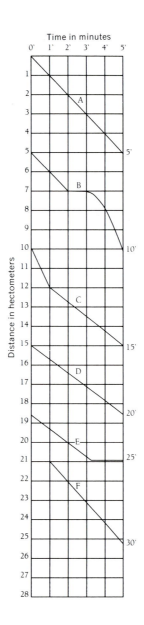

8. Recording of the progess of a moving body in terms of its movement and duration. During the first 5 minutes, the moving body traveled 5 hectometers with a uniform movement, section A. This pace (section B) was maintained for another 2 minutes, when a pause of one minute occurred. The moving body set off again with an accelerated movement until the tenth minute. This speed (section C) of 2 hectometers per minute was maintained until the end of the eleventh minute, when it gave way to a slower movement of 3 hectometers in 4 minutes which lasted throughout section D and a part of E until the twenty-first minute when a pause occurred. This pause of 3 minutes, which extended into section F, was followed by another period of uniform movement whose speed was slightly in excess of 100 meters per minute.

approach. He and they were intent on the same problem, namely, the inscription and analysis of what it had been possible to capture.

The fourth movement that influenced Marey's physiology was progress in the procedures of tonometry and stenography. Strangely enough, it would be acoustics that inspired the theoretician of informative graphism.

There were two main reasons for this: (1) a bridge between melodies and songs on the one hand, and sol-fa and short score on the other, had long been established – the famous sought-after passage from the invisible (the voice) to the visible (notes), or from a complex reality to its written substitute; and (2) biology at the time was concerned with a fundamental subject: understanding the heart's automatic workings, an uninterrupted movement that seemed to condition life itself. This rhythm was accompanied by noises, whose loudness, duration and order Chaveau himself had transcribed, using musical notation. Phonography was thus a companion to physiology. Moreover, what is alive (animal cries, human words) is characterized by its ability to emit sounds. It is not surprising that psychophysiologists (and especially Müller's German school) attempted to illuminate the mechanics of this sound production.

Marey's work cannot be understood without putting it in its original context and reconstructing all the factors relating to the collection, illustration and analysis of sound. It draws its inspiration from this (the image of life). Before coming to "acoustic representations," it is useful to go back to one of its pioneers, the elder Engramelle and his *La Tonotechnie, ou L'Art de noter les cylandres* (1775).

An Italian virtuoso had performed pieces for harpsichord at the court of the King of Poland, but had not wished to reveal the scores. The pieces were so appreciated that he agreed to play them again later. At this point, Engramelle, guest of the king and a clever mechanician, had the idea of placing a device he had invented underneath the musician's harpsichord. It was a "duplicator" or cylinder covered with blackened paper. In addition, he made a second keyboard with keys that corresponded to those of the real instrument so that anything played on it was ultimately transferred to the revolving cylinder discreetly set in motion. Because this was moving on a diagonal, the notes could not be superimposed or muddled. The hidden inscribing mechanism subsequently led to the construction of a machine (the bird organ), which replayed the piece of music at will.

Engramelle had long expounded on the art of notation by making cylinders on which nails of different lengths were arranged at precise distances from each other. Their uneven surface enabled the different sonorities to be restored. A refined musician would still have to evaluate the notes so that they could be translated. Then one could simply turn the handle at the proper speed to hear what had been sung or played: "It would be an advantage to those registering with a cylinder to have a good clock with a second hand so as to be sure of the duration of their cylinders' movement as well as the length of their melodies."[22] Engramelle lost no time making the most of his contraption. All kinds of music now could be taken "to barbarous countries": "How many places exist, even here in France, where divine worship is languishing for want of organists, and where these cylinders could compensate?"[23]

Sound phenomena were not inscribed directly with this machine. A sensitive, competent interpreter was required but such a translator would soon be dispensed with, and the song pictured directly. The device could be described as "reversible" because it captured the real (sounds) and then retransmitted them in their entirety. The cinematograph would later be characterized by the same ability to receive, retain and rerender.

We can imagine the rest. First, let us turn to the Viennese doctor, Ludwig Türck, who, inspired by the singer Manuel Garcia, produced the first laryngoscope (in 1857). By means of a flexible arm, a small mirror set in metal was brought to the back of the throat over the opening of the larynx. The mirror reflected the light and illuminated what had been hidden, namely the vocal apparatus. Its workings could now be examined.

Actually, in 1860, Johann Nepamuk Czermak of Pest University (Hungary) improved the process considerably by gaining a better view of the chords vibrating and relaxing. To this end, a beam of light from a nearby lamp, focused by a lens, was directed onto a mirror worn on the observer's forehead and held tight by an elastic support. This made it easy to direct the beam onto the second mirror located at the larynx, in the manner already mentioned. Thanks to this back and forth arrangement, the junction at the back of the throat was better lit. And if the metal arm was turned slightly so that its tip was inclined, the rear opening of the nostrils as well as the entrance to the eustachian tube were made visible. Pointed downward or upward, it constituted a successful means of exploring the isthmus of the gullet (figure 9).

Marey was not really interested in this type of examination but he did not reject it. He merely considered it rudimentary, too tied to "crude direct data." He constantly sought to imagine instruments that could go beyond the thresholds of perception and transcribe phenomena by themselves (autography, the language of nature). Nonetheless, the laryngoscope had a connection with his own approach. It allowed ephemeral words to be replaced by the movements that produced them; it was leading toward graphic inventions (phonautography). Moreover, Müller, as well as Hermann von Helmholtz, had constructed an "artificial larynx" using rubber and different membranes shaped like reeds, the whole imitating the apparatus of the human voice (and, if required, various animal cries): "From the tests done on the artificial larynx with membranous reeds and on the human larynx itself, the results of which tally perfectly on all essential points, it follows that the human organ is a reed with two membranous lips."[24] With this construction, German psychophysiology realized Marey's methodological aspiration: in order to understand, one must construct a

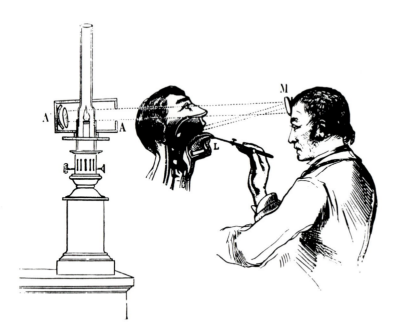

9. The laryngoscope. AA: light and reflecting lense; M: forehead mirror;
   L: stem of the larynx mirror. (From a document of the period.)

mechanical model able to imitate what is produced by the living organs (that is, movements, modifications and noises). In this way, we secure an understanding of their emergence, while at the same time making the processes visual. Acoustics (music, singing and vowels) would serve as the spearhead of physiology.

In his early work, Marey was interested by another breakthrough, made by Léon Scott de Martinville, Rudolf Koenig and Helmholtz. From the end of the eighteenth century, people sought to write down sound, if only as an aid to those born deaf and mute. The school of Condillac made particular efforts; knowing the importance of the senses and especially hearing (language), it was essential for them to find the means to compensate for such a serious handicap.[25]

In 1849, Scott de Martinville published his *Histoire de la sténographie depuis les temps anciens jusqu'à nos jours*, addressing in particular audiovisual transposition, that is, automated transcription of singing and other utterances. He wanted to fix speech mechanically. So what did this recording, patented at the Academy in 1857, consist of? The same elements were again brought together: something to pick up the vibrations, namely a horn with a flexible membrane as the receiver; a stylus to inscribe them; and a revolving cylinder, coated with lamp-black to record them. A specialist in mechanics and the construction of machines, Koenig took charge of its completion, thus dispensing with the services of a printer. The reading stenographed and represented itself directly through a tracing that corresponded to it; hence, a "kind of acoustics of and for the eyes."

One here recalls the "ocular harpsichord" of the elder Castel (1735), which had already transformed a musical notation into a picture (seven notes, seven colors). It found an admirer in Denis Diderot, who was fascinated with questions of translation and correspondence.

Koenig invented another device, using flames as pressure-gauges.[26] Marey wrote:

Here is the device that can be used to analyze sounds: a small metal container is placed at the end of a gas pipe and fitted with a thin burner where the gas is lit. One wall of the container is made of a thin rubber membrane. When a series of vibrations is transmitted to this membrane, the gas in the small container is in turn compressed and expanded, and the flame will undergo rapid alternations, rising and falling.... The eye, however, cannot directly perceive the number of these variations, which blend into a single visual impression. So there is a revolving mirror with four sides in which the flames are reflected. If I make this mirror revolve quickly by means of a handle, you see that each flame's image is a long, luminous ribbon, and that this ribbon has indentations....[27]

Letters and words were transformed into trails of fire!

Helmholtz, a follower of Müller, would fully realize optical–acoustic movement.[28] He achieved a synthesis of the relevant sounds and their harmonic combinations with the help of several tuning forks vibrating together. Mastery and understanding of sound were thus assured, and often preceded the simple "conquest of the image" in photography, even though both were following convergent paths. (The proof was that Félix Nadar himself described one of his goals as "an acoustic daguerreotype" and was working on it.[29]) The phonograph, a box in which tunes would be held and fixed, kept pace with the progress of the camera obscura.

Why was the picturing of the voice slightly ahead at times? Because the psychophysiologists and psychophysicists devoted a long period of time to its development, setting up suggestive experiments (as in Müller's "artificial larynx"). They regarded speech as what set man apart, his "soul" and his movement, just as the cry was characteristic of animals (the singing of birds, the buzzing of insects and so on). This was all the more reason to analyze it and clarify its workings. Later on, in the chapter on acoustics and the analysis of sound,

Marey would emphasize the importance of a later invention that would take systems of transfer a stage further.

Marey's problem was this: how to go on improving methods of capturing and translating phenomena in a web of inscription, where it became first visible, and then readable (that is, intelligible). In the nineteenth century, it gradually became possible to abandon early mechanical methods that were cumbersome and unreliable, in favor of graphic, and later numerical and electrical equivalents. The notions of signal and characters would gradually be modified. Marey thereby hoped to attain his goal: "the language of nature." Just as words could be metamorphosed, not into different words but into simple lines and flames, melodies could be written as a sequence of marks of varying length and height; there was no need for notation or the conventional scale. What was important throughout was eliminating the human intermediary, a screen that complicated, distorted and prevented access to reality. The same was true for the noises of the heart and the brisk movements of life: they were to make their own communication with us. The doctor or the biologist had to avoid getting in their way. Wasn't this also the goal of photography – letting the sun do its writing – to dispense with the intermediary of the painter and interpreter?

Thus, in one of his last books, *Movement* (1894), Marey duly celebrated what was in every way a decisive invention, Jean Carpentier and Charles Cros's automated melographic transcription. This shall be discussed later and is only mentioned here to demonstrate the importance of music and acoustics for Marey's research. Two transfer situations are to be distinguished in this regard:

First, "under each note on the keyboard of a harmonium, a tiny pair of bellows was placed, each of which was linked by a special tube with a corresponding pair, and commanded an inscription stylus. The series of styli were placed in a row and arranged in the order in which the different notes of music succeed one another...."[30] In this way, the performance would be transferred directly; instead of half notes, quarter notes, eighth notes and so on, the universal new notation was nothing but lengths. All the codes (artificial, cumbersome and distorting) were eliminated in order to construct "a melogram," similar to a phonogram, which would eventually be colored.

The second construction was more daring. Carpentier, to whom Marey refers, displayed the machine he had constructed, the repeater (which had been shown at the Universal Exhibition of Electricity in 1881), in *La Nature* of February 4, 1882 (figure 10). A piece still had to be played and recorded, but this time a perforator inscribed it onto cardboard across a sequence of gaps and solid areas. This was a shift from a printed strip to a stamped and more rigid one, which then activated a reproducing device called "the melotrope," which, placed on any piano, allowed the musical improvisation to be replayed on the spot. Ephemeral sounds were materialized as simple lengths or gaps; the music telegraphed itself. Not only did the notes inscribe themselves but they also inscribed their duration (chronophotography). This was now the epoch of Edison's phonograph, the "speaking machine." The door to electrography also had been opened.

The constant osmosis between physiology and mechanography should be kept in mind, specifically via the person of Marey himself, preeminent biologist-mechanician. He renewed our understanding of the organism through his sophisticated instruments, while biology would reciprocate by contributing to the invention of machines capable of imitating human performances (preserving the voice, for example, or flying in the air like a bird).

Marey always defended the theory of the "animal-machine," as long as this machine was no longer conceived as a simple assemblage of pulleys, wheels and wires, but rather as a veritable "animated motor," a living machine, at the source of activation (locomotion, voice and so on).

10. Carpentier's repeating melograph. An apparatus for recording and
reproducing music. Taken from *La Nature* (February 4, 1882).

These four converging trends – the work of Chauveau, the new methods of the German school of physiology, work in physics and parallel progress in acoustics – enable Marey's contribution to be seen more clearly. Marey would not merely improve on past discoveries, but would recapitulate them in the process of orienting his own research.

The first Marey – for we shall distinguish between two or three Mareys – was able to construct delicate instruments that enabled him to record, first of all, the most elusive internal movements (those of the artery, heart, muscle, lungs and so on). He was storming a fortress, attacking a two-fold problem: gaining access to both the minuscule and the hidden, without resorting to the bloody and intrusive methods of vivisection.

He began by perfecting existing instruments that had been elaborated upon but remained crude. With these he conducted successful experiments that strengthened his mastery of those revealing "tremors." The combination of elements was always the same: a sensor attached to the phenomenon (the internal movement), a conductor and an inscriber. It was a process of obtaining, translating and registering information, and it was constantly modified to accommodate increasingly subtle movements. The whole of Marey's biology and science rests on the invention of adequate procedures of collecting data. The first of Marey's apparatuses, the sphygmograph, should be emphasized because it inspired other early devices (the cardiograph, pneumograph, myograph, pantograph and so on). It opened the door for what followed.

Marey soon criticized Vierordt, the last of the German school of experimental physiology, for his obviously erroneous conclusions, and thus for his necessarily malfunctional method of externalization. Vierordt had transformed the understanding of circulation, the major problem of the time. He had abandoned the manometric approach and turned to an available sign (the pulse). He had found the tool that would permit the recording of its alternate rising and falling. At the instant of cardiac pressure, the arterial wall underwent a liquid shock, causing a wave of contraction that had to be "read" (the sphygmograph).

The result obtained, however, was strikingly crude and inexact. For even when taking the pulse by hand, a surge and ebbing can be felt, and the second phase seems at least twice as long as the first. Touch may often be deceptive but not in an indication as elementary as this. Yet Vierordt's traced line appeared as a curve whose two parts were perfectly equal:

> This discrepancy between the form of the trace and the tactile sensation felt when exploring an artery made the indications given by Vierordt's instrument seem questionable. We soon were convinced that the cause of error lay in the construction of the apparatus itself. In Vierordt's sphygmograph, the double lever, which was rather heavy, was balanced by a counterweight. An additional weight P was then used to squeeze the vessel with enough force to register the pulse.[31]

Marey put all his effort into the creation of a mechanical system that significantly improved on the German's: first, he aimed to make his with thin wood and aluminum. Seventeen centimeters in length, it would only weigh 220 g. This was precisely what had been made by Bréguet, "who has introduced new improvements to the mechanism in clocks which makes the plate move and whose regularity left much to be desired in other devices."[32]

The second innovation was without doubt the most crucial. The artery had to be squeezed a little in order to feel the pulse rise; this pressure would henceforth be applied by means of a fixed rubber spring which could be tightened as required. This avoided the heaviness of weights and counterweights, which crushed the vessel as well as the movement passing through it. The well-designed lever had two arms, the longer of which allowed for the trace's enlargement. Lastly, Marey replaced the steel point, which could potentially rub the paper too hard and add its own inertia, with a less rigid bird's quill, which neither slowed nor distorted the curve. Solidity, and even rigidity, were thus added to thinness and flexibility (figure 11a).

Was this the end of the problem? Far from it. First, the instrument had to be regulated; if it was too heavy, it did not work. If it was too thin or light, however, there was an equal danger that the results would suffer. Abrupt release of the lever caused "a tendency for it to lift further once the force pushing on it was removed."[33] Without a certain resistance to check it, the peak of the inscription was distorted and exaggerated, and therefore unreliable: "In certain cases," wrote Marey, "I apply a small spring to the lever, the pressure of which counters the effects of the acquired speed; this arrangement occurs in my sphygmograph"[34] (figure 11b).

There was another problem. Obtaining a curve was not enough; its soundness had to be verified. The meticulous Marey was quick to respond; otherwise he would run the risk of working with useless figures. But how could one test the tester of our movements and measure its sensitivity? It was no longer the fact, but the right of this fact that had to be imposed.

A first counter-test, applied each time one "sensor" was replaced by another, used the old instrument and then the new one. An evaluation was made of the proximity of the responses, as well as the discrepancy between them. Thus, Marey used the manometric method as a touchstone for experiments with his sphygmometer. The objection might be raised that a faulty procedure cannot, by definition, form the basis of judgment of a good one. The point was rather to see whether that one surpassed the other, producing what it had produced but with "pluses": "The sphygmoscope, registering the pulse of an artery, provides a graphic image identical to the one given by the sphygmograph applied to a vessel!"[35] (figure 12). Another more reliable evaluating technique was Franciscus Donders's

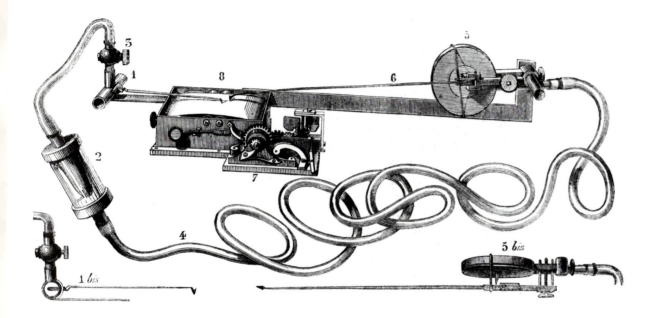

12. Chauveau's haemodromograph and a sphygmoscope simultaneously
recording pulsations. Taken from Marey, *Du mouvement*.

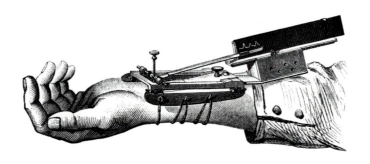

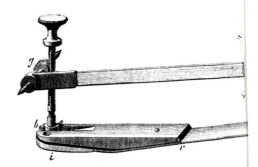

11a. Attachment of the sphygmograph to the wrist and inscription of
the trace of the pulse. Taken from Marey, *La Méthode graphique*.

11b. Marey's sphygmograph. Arrangement of the spring and inscribing
lever.

tactic, which allowed for standardization. A movement was produced, and its force and frequency were controlled. The sphygmograph, connected to the machine being manipulated, had to reproduce the oscillations and provide an image of these interventions. The instrument was required to register what the scientist provoked so that its "reliability" could then be assessed.

Having obtained accurate "tracings," information had to be extracted from them. Marey excelled in this regard. First, he quickly found a way to measure the speed of "propagation." He simply set two sphygmographs going at a certain distance apart; the distance being known, he could easily deduce the speed. He realized immediately that the pulse did not correspond to the passage of blood in the artery but to that of an independent and faster-moving wave (a vibratory effect). Many other more subtle tests would be carried out; thus, a decrease in speed could be noted at the extremity of the arterial tree, far away from the heart.

Without going into too much detail about the analysis of the various recordings, "the dicrotic line" deserves a mention (a surge producing a second peak). Marey correctly interpreted this as the result of two pulsations. The first and most important translated the dull striking of aortic blood by the jet stream spurting from the left ventricle. The second was due to the inevitable reflux of this surge against the sigmoid valves which had closed precisely in order to prevent it from flowing back. This double movement of the tracing, which hardly appeared in normal circumstances, was amplified and modified during certain disorders (deficiencies) either of the myocardium or of the aorta. The force of the heart as well as the valves was thus revealed, and in a sense exposed in the sphygmogram. Physiology had succeeded in its attempt to "lay the heart bare" and measure its workings (by breaking them down and assessing the amplitude as well as the frequency of rhythm). Cardiac revolution had been definitively linked to the peripheral phenomena that accompanied it and could be registered. Marey's reading was thus as important as his scriptural discoveries (a writing–reading system).

He continued to make increasingly sensitive and effective "recorders," and there was soon a cluster of cardiographs, myographs, pneumographs, pantographs and so on. These little machines, faithfully relaying and transmitting information, all stemmed from a similar schema. Marey's great originality lay in what he proposed: a sensor and a transmitter in which air was the mediator (figure 13). A rubber bulb at one end was connected to another bulb by a long tube. When the first was pressed, the second inflated. The second was able to transcribe the pressure with a lever with a tracing quill at its free end. Here, then, were the essential elements of a device that allowed not exploration of the body, but the collection of all the things that were elusive: the tiniest movements and the slightest unfoldings, such as those of the thoracic cage, from which the pneumograph enabled breathing to be analyzed. As one advance brought another, it would soon be possible to undertake comparative studies based on the results of the various devices: one connected to the lungs, the other to arterial movement (the beginnings of the vast cardiopulmonary domain).

The cardiograph calls for a word of commentary. Marey, working with Chauveau, first placed the bulbs inside the cardiac cavities (the auricles and ventricles). Here, his device reverted back to the old method of probes and catheters. They began, then, by violent "sampling," using horses, which were able to tolerate it. They even managed to record three curves simultaneously because they were hoping to capture the successive stages or possible synchronicity of the movements (figure 14). Three levers thus inscribed the play of the auricles, that of the ventricles, and that of the beating of the heart against the chest wall. It is difficult to imagine everything Marey and Chauveau would gather from these notations. Marey wrote: "By looking at the line of the external beating of the heart, it was possible to know everything that was happening within this organ."[36] These two adjectives,

13. Drawing of a pneumatic sensor and transmitter for transmitting movement over a distance. Taken from Marey, *Du mouvement*.

external and internal, should be noted in passing, since the first essentially expressed the second. It was simply a matter of learning how to project one onto the other. Among the various results, however, it was noted that the force of the right ventricle relative to that of the left was "approximately in the ratio of 1 to 3."[37]

Marey would soon replace this procedure, however, with a more reliable and less violent one. It would be applied to the human body, whereas the earlier one could only be performed on the horse. It involved a simple, hollow, wooden cap, slightly elliptical in shape, "with a spring at its bottom that can be adjusted as necessary. This spring is fitted with a small ivory plate that presses on the area where the heartbeat is produced."[38] This apparatus, whose elements, after all, might vary (a moveable cap, or bulb, or funnel or cone, sphygmographic lever, transmitting system, cylinder), defined the polygraph (figure 15). It seems the tracing obtained was exactly the same as the one produced by the directly exploratory system. The latter was abandoned, then, because it was so cumbersome. A new instrument in principle causes the disappearance of a cruder one: instruments contribute to their own obsolescence.

If there was a problem – sometimes certain forces could not be registered – Marey was quick to put into effect a methodological principle spread widely by the German school (particularly the Weber brothers [Ernst and Wilhelm]): simulation with a mechanical model. Thus, a pump would be constructed that pushed the blood, at regular intervals, into tubes equipped with valves. If readings could not be taken from the living body, work would be done on its double; on the substitute, one could practice the art of detecting functional "tremors."

Imitating the movements of life remained essential. Marey indeed considered work on synthesis – that is, artificial reproduction – to be as indispensable as that on analysis and data collection. It was a theme of his research from the beginning. In addition to the cardiac pump, he attempted to construct many other machines capable of highly complex operations, such as the thoracic cage – with rhythmic pulmonary ventilation and displacement of the ribs.

Marey's techniques were becoming increasingly successful. Nothing was an obstacle, not even the brain (thought). How was this possible? First, a chronographic tuning fork made measuring time more precise: 500 vibrations per second would trace a fine, wavy line in which each tiny oscillation represented 1/500th of a second. Second, Marey had at one time been concerned with muscular contraction. The German school had been well ahead of him (Emil du Bois-Reymond, Helmholtz, Christoph Aeby, Gabriel Valentin and others). Helmholtz had used a myograph (in 1850), but the results were rather crude. Marey's could record the slightest nuances. In his version, a flexible clamp held the muscle transversally and communicated its "swelling-shortening" to the inevitable recording needle. It also was known that a blow to the nerve, or a discharge of static electricity produced a greater twitch than direct stimulation of the fiber, the motor agent. In this, Marey was following the lead taken by electrophysiology, although he had considered a different option (partly a dead end) extoled by Helmholtz.[39] I mention this because it is a constant: the importance

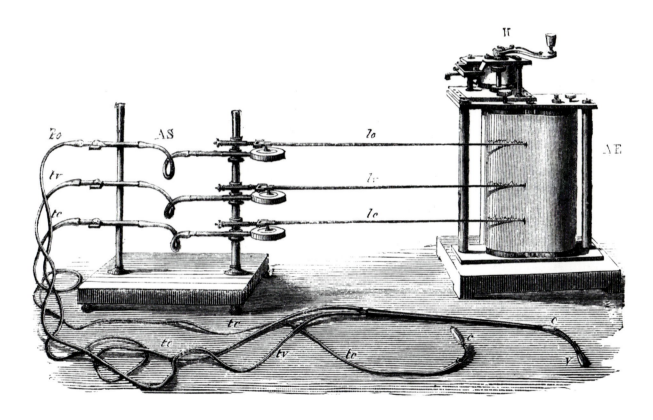

14. Chauveau and Marey's cardiograph. Taken from Marey, *Du mouvement*.

given to the role of acoustics. It was possible to hear the noises and cracklings of our muscle twitches: not colored but musical movement![40]

Where these paths cross, Marey, from 1868, was boldly attempting something new: between a sharp sensation aroused in a human or animal and the reaction produced and localized by the myograph, there occurred "a psychic act." The current had, of necessity, passed through the cortex of the will. Its duration would be immediately known; it also seemed perfectly feasible to examine what caused it to slow down or accelerate. This circuit thus began to be explored. "Precise experiment and exact measurement," wrote Marey, "have begun to appear even in the phenomena of thought."[41] I discuss this chronometric experimentation to show that the science of data collection was beginning to affect the cerebral. The darkness shrank before science. There were no limits to how far it could go; it could measure "the time will takes to travel a certain distance"!

Marey already had laid the foundations for studying the physiology of life; that is, for studying internal dynamics, with both its sudden as well as continuous movements. He had captured their rhythm, frequency and amplitude. He had been able to calculate forces and expenditures of energy.

His originality lay in the use of the following elements: a sensitive sensor, a transmitter whose inertia is negligible, an inscription device adapted to sinuous writing, and a synthesizing device to be used for verification. There was a leitmotif in Marey's work taken from Marcellin Berthelot, the synthetic chemist: we only have real knowledge of what we ourselves have reconstructed. Of the four elements above, it is the first and last that are the most important.

The body, swept by waves and multiple fluxes, is a theater of imperceptible noises and

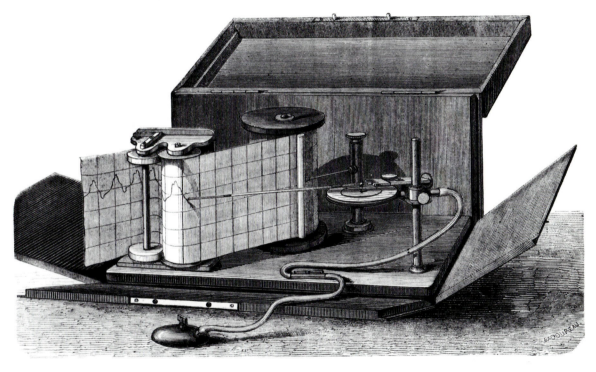

15. Polygraph for registering various internal movements of the human body (heart, lungs and so on). Taken from Marey, *Du mouvement*.

murmurs. Marey was able to capture them, enlarge them, if necessary, and above all transfer them onto a cylinder that made them visual and allowed their evaluation. With the abundance of results I have described, Marey's work might be complete; first the sphygmograph, then its related devices the cardiograph, pneumograph, pantograph and, most importantly, the myograph.

As with the sphygmograph, Marey again borrowed from the German school, as he readily admits when tracing its evolution (Helmholtz, 1850; Aeby, 1862; Valentin, 1863; Adolf Fick, 1864[42]). However, he would perfect its mechanics and functioning:

> I decided to construct a new myograph and, despite myself, to make what was already a complex assembly of instruments even more complex. This is because none of the devices employed up until now seemed accurate enough to me. Some included far too much inertia, while others produced graphics that were difficult to read or whose dimensions were too large.[43]

Thanks to the myograph that he now modified, he was entering, willy-nilly, a new field: the neuromuscular – acts of locomotion and volition. From internal movements and their muffled pulsations, he would turn to external movements (in the air, in water and on the ground). The second Marey, if my divisions are accepted, emerged around 1870.

The overriding theme would not change (on the one hand, the unrivaled importance of the sensor in the sequence outlined; on the other, the necessity of reconstituting what had been analyzed), yet everything would take on a new light. The style of recording as well as reassembling would emerge totally modified.

The following three conclusions end this discussion of who I call the first Marey:

First, the injustice and inadequacy of one version of the history of biology should be noted. In the nineteenth century, two names seem to eclipse all others: Claude Bernard and Louis Pasteur. Marey apparently is not thought to be in the same league. Not only does he deserve to take his place alongside them; his own discoveries have contributed more to the evolution of culture, society and indeed science itself than those of his peers.

A curious incongruity might be noted here. Bernard and Pasteur upheld more or less vitalist approaches. In Marey's opinion, however, they did not arrive at an understanding of life itself; indeed, they betrayed it. Marey, meanwhile, claiming to be "an out and out mechanist," and applying mechanics to animal life with rare determination, successfully penetrated its subtleties and slipped between its swiftest movements (first internal, then external). It was a paradox, then, that this adamant physicist would prove to be the most physiological in approach, the one to delve deepest into the hidden sanctuary of animal life.

Second, the direct consequence of this was not only thinly veiled attacks against Bernard and Pasteur – the laboratory practitioners – but, a little later, a demand for a totally different kind of work place. Marey wanted zoological gardens, agronomical parks and, especially, physiological stations in order to facilitate the authentic study of nature. And his call was answered: the city of Paris gave him use of a large space near the Porte d'Auteuil. In August 1882, Jules Ferry, Minister of Public Instruction, argued in parliament for a public institute, the construction of the "Avenue des Princes" – an enormous track, sheds and studios.

Neither the biochemist nor the physiologist, according to the rather acerbic Marey, was really studying the functions of life, still less the great animal species such as the horse and the camel. Vivisection was poisoning their research and provided no understanding of the regular play of life. Marey's books are filled with criticisms aimed at the experimenters who began by upsetting or destroying what they claimed to be analyzing. The physiology of the physiologists offered little or nothing: Why?

The following quotation provides a representative answer: "The secretion of the glands under normal conditions is very different from what is collected by artificial means. Thus the pancreatic juice taken from an animal on which a fistula has been performed is chemically different from that normally secreted into the duodenum by the gland."[44] Marey did not shrink from large claims such as this.

In the journal, *La Nature*, he went even further: "Laboratories, in France at least, are sad, poor and unhealthy places where researchers are condemned to live in the forlorn hope of discovering the properties of tissues and the functions of living organs. It is there that the effects of drugs on the living organism are detected, along with those of poisons and various chemical and physical agents...."[45] Here, one can discern an attack on the views of Bernard and his use of toxic substances as tools of analysis.

There is a further point. The vitalists still separated "function" from "structure." Consequently, morphology hardly seemed a worthwhile discipline, and they ignored it. But Marey considered it fundamental: energy was bound up with machinery and arose wholly from it. Movements, whether internal or external, flowed from the conformation and arrangement of the organs. This anatomy was not a reiteration of the body's machinery; but first captured its arrangement of parts (first graphic image), and then attempted to infer its dynamic. On a simple surface – a bone, for instance – he located the chambers corresponding to the muscle attachments, then the grooves where the tendons fit, the rounded areas worn shiny from rubbing, curvatures linked to traction and so forth. As shall be seen below, the flight of birds was linked to the shape of their skeleton, to the length and volume of their muscles and to the relative dimensions of their limbs. Hence, the Mareyan assertion that "the physiological function can be explained on anatomical grounds."[46] No less was to be expected from the specialist in animal mechanics.

It is true that his vehemence would later be tempered. Thus:

It has often been said that anatomy is not enough to explain the physiology of the organs. This is true, particularly of certain organs: the form and structure of the brain do not explain thought; anatomical study of the spleen has not yet told us what this voluminous organ is for; but this is not the case for the locomotive apparatus. By looking at the articular surfaces we are perfectly able to understand the direction and extent of the movements which an articulation provides.[47]

If I add to this that the examples given (the brain and particularly the spleen) to lessen the importance of studying the substratum alone, came straight out of Bernard, in whose work they were touchstones, the distance between the two becomes clear. One might also note that Marey's apparent concession in the quotation actually allowed him to strengthen his own thesis (locomotion, particularly in light of Marey's contention that life is movement and nothing else). Graphic techniques would demonstrate this, revealing an animal architecture and eliminating the nonessential.

Clearly Marey was no longer following the path taken by the biology of his day. He cast aside what it revered and focused on what it rejected. With him, "a new spirit" was ushered in. But one should not conclude from this that Marey now championed the observation of naturalists. He relied even more than others on complex "instruments," and on the places set up for them (research stations). He ruled out direct examination and criticized those practicing in laboratories for their trust in sensory results:

Vivisection in itself is inadequate for the study of biology; all it does is lay bare the phenomenon.... All it reveals to our senses is what they can directly perceive. But you have seen in physics how little our senses tell us, so that we are constantly obliged to use apparatuses in order to analyze things.[48]

The semiadversary of the physiological science of his day in no way disowned science in general or this science in particular, but rather its direction.

The third, brief, somewhat related conclusion is our attachment to a "myth of depth." Life, under these conditions, could not be reduced to a few noises, or described by a few curves, even though Marey would have liked to locate it here entirely. He was transposing life perhaps, but not really capturing it. To shift is neither to experience nor to know. Was it not necessary to go beyond appearances?

Marey tirelessly responded to this simultaneously scientific and methodological objection. Clearly, it was insufficient merely to learn how to inscribe (writing); it was equally important to know how to read and decipher. Moreover, Marey had likened biology to an exegetic science (writing–reading), against leading physiologists whom he considered too preoccupied with basic principles: "If I had to use a metaphor, I would compare the study of natural sciences with the work of archaeologists deciphering inscriptions written in an unknown language and trying several meanings for each sign...."[49]

The whole of his work had consisted in showing what one could learn from a curve, which was not merely a simple "reproduction." It was from and with the curve that forces could initially be calculated. It was easy to obtain the mass of the body as well as the speed it was going (chronobiology); from this one could induce the force that had set it in motion, the work expended to produce this action. This trajectory always had to be questioned and interpreted. Not only were the slightest nicks and notches in the line due to certain factors, but they enabled the determination of resistances as well as impulses.

Marey thus refused to go down the sloping twists and turns of the visceral. His science brought to the surface what was thought inaccessible, eliminated the superfluous (interference) and kept only the essential (the message from the lines themselves). He directly questioned not only our senses, which deceive us, but also languages that lead us astray: natural language, which is unreliable and scientific language, which often appears too hastily and then becomes contrived.

The "trace," in contrast, was to be considered nature's own expression, without screen, echo or interference: it was faithful, clear and, above all, universal. All we had to do was translate what nature itself told us about itself. All we had to do was listen!

Marey's success (first his sphygmograph, followed by the cardiograph and lastly the myograph) was the result of his meticulousness, his patience and his determination. He perfected the "telescriptors," which his predecessors, biologists and physicists, had still not adequately "refined." "It has been said," wrote Marey, "that my work is 'always the same old thing.' This assessment... is the greatest reward for my efforts."[50] What was given as a criticism described him well and, contrary to what was thought, became the highest praise. "The same old thing" was, moreover, a simple thing: the capture of the phenomenon (the sensor) beyond what the senses or words could take in or retain. Graphic images explicitly established themselves as the phenomenon's own language – one could only know the phenomenon through this sort of "spoken word-writing."

16. Recording system in movement.

The Second Adventure

It seems striking that in 1868, in *Du mouvement dans les fonctions de la vie*, Marey was still concerned with the myograph, the device he had used to study muscular contraction and tetanus and to measure the speed of nerve impulse. For in 1873, in his new book, *Animal Mechanism*, he abandoned his earlier points of reference – cardiac cycles, ventilation, the twitch of a frog's leg at the application of an electric impulse. Marey entered an entirely new domain: the running of the horse, the flight of birds, walking, jumping and human gesture; and later the swimming of fish, the course of a jellyfish and the movement of flies. He ultimately attempted the most difficult subject of all: not only microscopic, single-celled organisms but the red and white corpuscles that move within the capillary vessels (those of the newt's mesentery). This led him again to a problem he had put aside, namely, the speed of blood (haemodromometry), although this should not be considered as a step backward.

Roughly speaking, then, 1870 marked a break: it was the year in which Marey completed "the externalization" he had already started.[1] Before this, he had brought what moved inside (the vegetative) to the outside. From now on, he took squarely into account the already visible, which he would attempt once again to register through a system of notation. His methods, apparatuses (especially the means of "capturing" data [figure 16]) and observations would be transformed alongside what he examined. This second Marey was not simply an extension or completion of the first, but a radical renewal.

The questions involved are still apparently minor – the beating of a butterfly's wing – but the thesis here, which Chapter 3 will focus on, is that, from industry to the arts to communications, society would be transformed by Marey's work. Incalculable effects would be garnered from extremely specific analysis. The twentieth century owes a great deal to Marey and his discoveries. Thus, it is all the more important to examine these findings before considering their consequences and repercussions.

My analysis of the second Marey also begins with the horse. It will be recalled that Jean-Baptiste Chauveau owed part, perhaps the core, of his success to his choice of experimenting with this animal, which allowed relatively easy readings of the automatic workings and vibrations of the heart. This was a path Marey followed, at least for a time.

In 1870, the horse was again the center of attention, but from the outside, so to speak, for its dauntless gallop. This had long interested naturalists. Marey took up where they left off and simply extended their work. Why such an interest in the horse and its speed? I have to enter the field where the battle was played out that produced the second Marey. In a word, optical sensors would replace the mechanical or air-driven ones used until then, and produce (if my analysis of their role is accepted) startling results, the foremost being an understanding of violent movements which were almost imperceptible because of their speed.

The horse's role in nineteenth-century society was the same as the car's in the twentieth. It participated in the main economic activities (transport, agriculture, even war). This is no doubt why hippology enjoyed a great surge of interest. Some of hippology's results should be mentioned briefly because Marey would exploit them when he was not finding fault with them.

Although not specifically concerned with the "way the horse moves," the famous royal equerry Claude Bourgelat had mentioned it in his *Traité de la conformation extérieure du cheval, de sa beauté et de ses défauts* (1776), and also in *Eléments d'hippiatrie* (1750).[2] His aim was to present ways of assessing its strength and capacity. To this end, he offered hippometric tables (length, breadth and so-called flat proportions of various parts, especially the head), which would help in detecting hidden constitutional defects (walking on the points of its rear hooves and so on[3]): "When wishing to buy a horse, one must not pass lightly over even the smallest part of it; examination must be scrupulously exact. If you have to watch the feet from behind. . . ."[4] Bourgelat was interested in the animal's walk and pace, and very much in its feet. Ultimately, the "trot" seemed the best way of judging it.

This is why "the races" became so important: "There has been too much pretense that [the races] can be reduced to the level of a simple pleasure. They have been, and continue to be, regarded by some – supposedly serious people – as merely an excuse for dissipation, luxury and elegance," wrote an expert.[5] This was quite wrong: "A horse runs fast and for a long time only when to the size of its lungs is added the strength and energy of its muscles."[6] "Motor evidence" was thus preferable to that gained from morphology. That might well be the case; but how – by what methods? – could movement at such speed be captured? This economic and scientific question would be a continuing preoccupation (selection and odography – the "black box" – respectively).

A tricky problem now presented itself: the earlier internal organs, though hidden, were less perplexing, as if their movements seemed more easily grasped. To begin with, apparatuses such as the heart and artery essentially formed an indissociable "whole," while locomotive apparatuses consisted of rotatory elements and sections which moved separately (two wings, four legs). They had a different way of moving. Furthermore, when an animal ran or flew away, it could not be followed, not even visually; while the heart and lungs necessarily accompanied us – eternal and indispensable equidistance. They could thus have fixed recording devices placed on or around them: bands, straps and belts. But how could contact be maintained with something that flew away or kept changing speed, such as a horse that was walking and then suddenly broke into a trot or gallop? If we looked into the sky, we would be totally overwhelmed by the variety and unpredictability of the insect's zig-zags – its hovering was movement in immobility!

In short, Mareyan transcription seemed compromised, faced with movements that were elusive, rapid, multiple and furtive. Examining "the external" must have seemed a step forward, but the reality was that the whole approach had unwittingly begun with the easiest subjects. It would be necessary for Marey to modify his recording procedures; it seemed doubtful that previous ones would be adequate. So much the better.

Thus, Marey entered the storm. He was not the first. His predecessors had had recourse to various ingenious strategies and instruments and had produced some not trivial results. These must now be considered, in order to be able to assess Marey's differences and, before long, the dramas he found himself in.

From the many standard works on the subject, let us examine the celebrated book by the veterinarians Georges Goiffon and Antoine Vincent: *Mémoire artificielle des principes relatifs à la fidèle représentation des animaux tant en peinture qu'en sculpture* (1779).[7] This fundamental work deserves mention (and Marey often refers to it) because it had a noticeably "visual" approach to the horse – trotting, galloping, in all its gaits – for the use of painters and sculptors as well as riders.

The introduction's remarks could have been made by Marey: "The most careful inspection will never be enough to unravel the successive and harmonic order of the limbs: the speed with which they move together or, in turn, disturb, so to speak, the sight of those who would observe them and follow them or analyze their movement...."[8] This is a distinctly Mareyan theme – the champion of optical analysis was the first to distrust the act of looking.

To make their lessons easier, the two doctors turned to stenography – a shortened form of writing – because they thought that the painter did not have the time to refer to written texts for instruction: "As far as possible, we replace words with other means of prompting and awakening ideas, so that the artist, palette or roughing chisel in hand, can recall and retrace all the things that might help him."[9] This was no doubt what made Goiffon and Vincent so well known; the hippographic side of it has been somewhat forgotten. "The means we use," they add, "consist principally of a collection of tables, lists and pictures made up of lines, letters and numbers; geometric figures and picturesque figures. A widely accepted property of well-drawn and appropriately presented figures is that they do the work of many words. This property was perhaps never so real or useful as in our artificial Memory."[10] Without this vademecum, without the flat, ichnographic drawing, the plastic artist would, in the opinion of Goiffon and Vincent, see little or nothing, even in the presence of the living model. He had to be armed, equipped with numbers, measurements and angles. A veritable unforgettable mnemotechnic treatise! A horse transformed into numbers and a few lines! Here was an eighteenth-century text, a hundred years before Marey, mixing elements that he would later associate: movement, animal physiology and art.

The two veterinarians used at least two reliable methods to ensure the success of their project. And what they would call "hodochronometry" would form a large part of their teachings (measuring times and distances traveled as well as modes of locomotion).

The first was the technique of "prints," or the scrupulous examination of the "traces" of horseshoes on a soft track, which indicated the successive position of the legs in motion. Sometimes, of course, the hoof marks seemed to blend into one another, but there were ways of distinguishing them. Apart from the fact that soles could be nailed to the horse's hooves to make them distinct, two prints superimposed also could be recognized by the fact that the doubling of the steps widened the edges of these microcraters "just like pressing two different seals into the same piece of soft wax."[11]

This modest method was not their invention; hippologists had used it before. It may have evolved from the lessons and books of "dance masters" (choreographers) that abounded, such as Pierre Rameau's 1725 work, *Un Abrégé de la nouvelle méthode dans l'art d'écrire et de tracer toutes sortes de danses de villes*.[12] This clever stenography was not only linked to music but, like music, it took into account measure – the time taken to raise the leg, bend it and so on.

Doctors made their own use of the method. The soles of a patient's feet would be coated with rouge, and he or she would then walk on a roll of paper with a line down the middle. The distance between his or her steps, the angles and types of pressure would be examined, revealing many symptoms, such as possible abasia (inturned and outturned feet and so on). In short, the eighteenth century was not lacking in resourcefulness. The desire had been expressed and, in a sense, had been realized for what some called a "traceology."

Goiffon and Vincent's second strategy was listening to the sound of the horse's hooves striking hard ground, or beats: "The order of beats in relation to the legs which make them heard is such that if we call the front right A, the front left B, the hind right C and the hind left D, and start counting the beats from A, they occur in a walk in the order A, D, B, C," thus four sounds.[13] But in the amble, which is faster by half, AC and BD were heard: the two right legs followed by the two left (a lateral biped effect). The faster trot would be written AD and BC (diagonal biped effect). Goiffon and Vincent ultimately identified several types of movement in addition to walking, with its four beats (the ear was more informative than the eye): the amble, the trot and the gallop.

The quadruped ought to be described as a multibiped: either the two right legs and the two left (the amble), or a right in conjunction with a left (the trot), or again the two front legs followed by the two hind ones (gallop). This might be set out schematically as follows:

A, B   A, D, B, C (walk)

            AC–BD   (amble)

            AD–BC   (trot)

C, D   AB–CD   (gallop)

Imprints and noises were the guide here. Marey would obviously criticize these indirect investigations, since they were too dependent on the eyes and ears. To address the same problem – the analysis of locomotion – with a more reliable methodology, he used his own recorders (bulbs and air-based transmitters). He adapted the cardiograph apparatus already used on the horse for the new situation.

He put "rubber balls" connected to recorders under the hooves. As the horse walked or ran, these were crushed; the recording cylinders then noted changes in pressure for each hoof's respective position and the speed of the changes. Marey's chronography quickly turned the successive movements and duration of contact and raising of the legs into a kind of notation, a readable sequence consisting only of lines: "I thought these figures would be more striking if transformed into a kind of musical notation in which the essentials were reduced to two lines. The steps of the right foot were recorded in white on the lower line, while those of the left foot, higher up, were recorded in diagonal hatched lines...."[14]

In what respect was this apparatus superior? It clearly picked up everything that the other already did, but it could also tell us how the transition from one style (the trot, for example) to another (the gallop) occurred. It easily ascertained the transitions between speeds and also measured their duration (chronobiology captured both time and space).

The details and consequences of the analysis shall be examined later; it seems Marey actually sidestepped the matter (see Chapter 3, below). For now, his immediate concern was to replace his "pneumatic shoe": "These apparatuses wear out very quickly on the road, but last for quite some time on the artificial soil of the riding-school. For the experiments we have done on ordinary roads and on pavement, we have had recourse to another instrument...."[15] Admittedly, it differed only slightly from the earlier one: the hoof was either lifted or lowered. Here, a sort of leather bracelet was placed, not beneath the hoof, but around the fetlock (near the hock) and was fastened by buckles. Four transmitting tubes that were uncrushable from outside, one for each hoof, indicated the raising and lowering of the step. With one hand, the rider held the box where the styluses would record the results (figure 17). However, when the horse galloped at full speed, the rider could no longer hold the recorder. It was thus secured in a flat box which was strapped to the rider's back like a soldier's pack. The harnessing system was also strengthened: "The impact on the ground is so violent that it would instantly have broken the devices used earlier."[16]

What was Marey's contribution in relation to his predecessors? He verified what the veterinarians had already patiently gathered: "We must not forget that Vincent and Goiffon's method only expressed a succession of movements observed by the eye or the ear, and that it was only as exact as the individual observer."[17] It was, above all, graphic curves that specified and emphasized what hippologists barely mentioned. In one phase of the gallop, for instance, the horse supported itself on its left hind leg alone. Marey revealed the undulation of its leg action and also noticed that, for an instant, the horse's four feet were off the ground! This (verifiable) observation was of great interest (figures 18, 19, 20, 21).

If the horse gave him a surprise, the bird in flight put him in an instant dilemma. In this

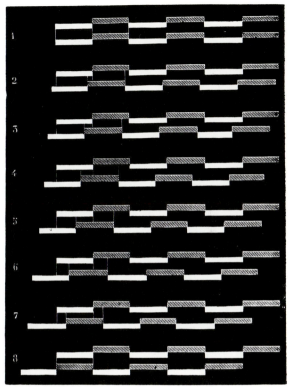

17. Chronographic study of the paces of a horse wearing pneumatic
detectors on each leg. The rider holds the chronograph in his hand.

1. Amble (all authors).
Broken amble (Merche).
2. High-stepping walk (Bouley).
Ordinary walk of a racehorse (Mazure).
3. Broken amble (Bouley).
Racking gait (Lecoq).
4. Normal walk (Lecoq).
5. Normal walk (Bouley, Vincent and
Goiffon, Soleysell, Colin and others).
6. Normal walk (Raabe).
7. Loose-limbed trot.
8. Ordinary trot.

18. Fourth moment of the gallop. Taken
from Marey, "La Locomotion animale."

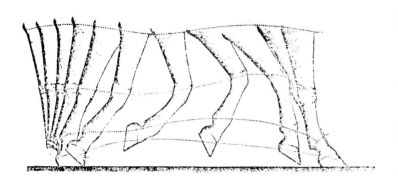

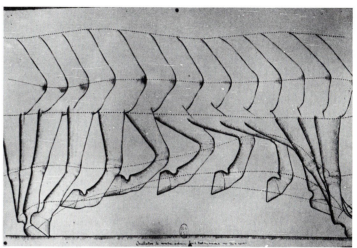

19. Oscillations of the front limb of the horse walking. The interval between positions is 1/10 second.

20. Oscillations of the front limb of the horse galloping. The interval between positions is 1/25 second.

case, there were neither traces on the ground nor "noises" (the beats). If, around 1870, he was able to solve the problem presented by the fiery steed, aerial motion would force Marey to modify his earlier tactics. How could aerial motion be recorded?

Although the actual "revolution in methods" would not occur until 1878, it can be anticipated here in the need to "re-examine" procedures that, up to then, had been irreproachable, indeed, infallible.

Around 1870, then, there were three relative innovations in the machinery used. If it is correct to assume that "the indicator" determined discoveries – the invisible could finally be seen – it will be no surprise that ingenuity first occurred in this area and that through this promising and sometimes baffling results could be reaped. All of the efforts to improve and refine "the indicator" should therefore be examined.

A more complex "indicator" was now needed to accommodate small, fluttering movement – that of a fly, a wasp or a sparrow. It was no longer feasible to use the heavy gear of harnesses, wires and cylinders; a delicate wing could obviously not support that.

Not surprisingly, Marey first thought of working from sound – a constant motif in his research and approach – produced by the insect flying and beating the air (for example, the mosquito's humming and other buzzing noises caused by the movement of the wing sheaths). I should note that Helmholtz had pursued this approach: the frequency of the vibrations produced sounds and these sounds expressed the vibrations. Thus, one could be judged by the other. But Marey would soon be disenchanted: "As the insect approaches the ear, the tonality rises; it falls as the insect moves away."[18] Equidistance alone could ensure objective assessment. It would not be possible for long "to estimate, based on the tonality of sound produced by a flying insect, the absolute frequency of the strokes of its wings."[19] The approach was abandoned, but I mention it because, faced with the problem, Marey tried to introduce an old method used in cardiography (the phonocardiography practiced

21. Horse walking, 1886

by Chauveau). If the animal stayed in one place, noise would constitute the best indication of its movement.

Marey now fell back on a type of writing that was direct and original, though still awkward — one that was daring in, and in spite of, its simplicity. Using fine tweezers, the insect "is placed in such a manner that, with each movement, one of its wings brushes lightly against the blackened paper. Each of these contacts removes a portion of the black powder covering the paper."[20] Unable to use the standard gear (strap and cylinder), the phenomenon was mechanographed without any intermediary. Marey thus renewed the tactic of "imprints" and obtained a series of short, delicate shadings. The insect was made to "register" its cinematic trajectory.

Once again, the same means used to examine locomotion on land (marks) were used here, but the results were rather questionable. Marey recognized that "the wing that brushes against the cylinder is not moving at its normal speed, and its revolutions are fewer as the friction increases."[21] Either such slight contact had to be made that there would be a danger of registering nothing, or the wing would touch the cylinder to the detriment of precision.

New devices had to be invented; Marey thus embarked on a semioptical method. To the tip of the wing in flight, he attached a thin gold disc onto which he projected a beam of sunlight, as the wasp spun around. He sought thereby to make visible the incessant oscillations of the dancing point (an elongated "8" actually appeared). Here, in 1873, Marey transposed Charles Wheatstone's technique, which involved a vibrating stem with a minute, shiny sphere. Rudolf Koenig later added a stylus that registered its countless vibrations. Marey was naturally won over by results so like his own.

Let us note, in this respect, that Jules Antoine Lissajous's ingenious machine (*Etude optique des mouvements vibratoires*, 1873) was not yet available to inspire Marey, although Marey paid due respect to him in *La Méthode graphique*. The physicist was able to attach small metallic mirrors, first to one vibrating tuning fork and then to a second. Light fell on the first, was reflected in the second and finally traced the combined back-and-forth movements of both on a screen. If the two blades oscillated neither together nor with the same amplitude (they were set in motion accordingly), an infinite number of figures would be produced (figure 22).

This was a major advance in two ways: (1) by combining all the movements, all the interferences could be drawn; and (2) in addition, a new, more effective version of Koenig's "ocular harpsichord" or "manometric flames" was produced – a pleasing transformation of harmonics or "relations" into a visual mode.

Marey was literally enchanted by this spectral "harmonigraph," not only because it translated acoustics immediately into curves but also represented a sort of flashing and automated industrial production. In this pantographic creation, *La Méthode graphique* rightly recognized an example of its own spirit (the art of marks and their multicoiling, a "music" of the eyes).

In all hypotheses, vibrations and shapes were interchangeable: the fastest movements could be "seen" either directly or on the screen. The method, however, was, as I have said, semioptical. Though one could better observe the wasp's flight in all directions, humans were still prisoners of sight, unable to record the result mechanically.

For want of anything better, some of the old apparatus could be used, as long as it was modified, and more robust birds with long wings and broad pectorals were used; flies, wasps and butterflies would have to be abandoned! The myograph could then come back into effect.

I must again stress Marey's approach here: the improvement of an old device. He was partially successful. First, instead of transmitting signals and information through a column of air, he used electrical exchange: "At the tip of the pigeon's wing is a device which opens or closes a current depending on whether it is raised or lowered." This electromechanical

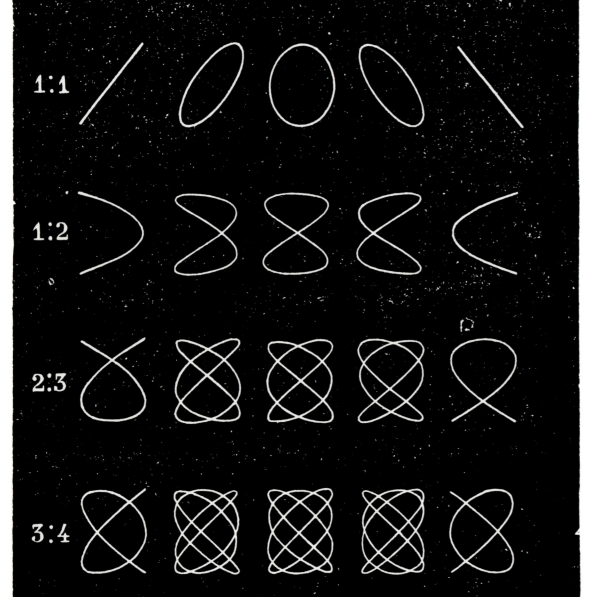

22. Lissajous's graphic notations, taken
from his "Etude optique des
mouvements vibratoires."

contact made it possible to count the wing revolutions, their amplitude and duration as well as the synchronicity of the two wings. The triad was still in place – "a receiver, a transmitter and a recorder" – but the second element was replaced with a more reliable and sensitive one (figure 23).

Physiology did not "steal" this element, if I can speak in such terms; physiology was actually what brought electrical energy into being (Alessandro Volta, Luigi Galvani, Carlo Matteuci and others). Physicists then benefited from it in the science and art of exchange and communication of all kinds (Louis Bréguet's dial-equipped telegraph and Giovanni Caselli's original and remarkable pantelegraph deserve mention). Finally, biologists, starting with Emil du Bois-Reymond, incorporated this "medium" into their schema and into their laboratories, taking up what their learned colleagues had so ably manipulated.

Nevertheless, Marey would soon have to produce a more complex system for it to work: wires still had to link the bird to a terminal and, thus, to recording cylinders. The perimeter of the bird's flight had to be restricted, without taking away its relative freedom of movement.

However, this was not the main problem. Until now, shortenings and elongations, or ascents and descents, were "read" in an essentially "linear" way. However, the pigeon moved in relation to three mutually perpendicular axes (hence, the urgent need for stereography): from low to high, right to left and vice versa, and from backward to forward all at once; with an additional kind of retrogression (caused by braking). It moved in all directions; it therefore had to carry at least three transmitting levers, each mounted on a moveable fitting so that it could turn in any direction. A triple pick-up would have to be used. If I add that it was necessary to slow down movements that were too rapid, and to accelerate those that were too slow, so as to "get them all in," we can see how cumbersome the contraption was (figures 24, 25).

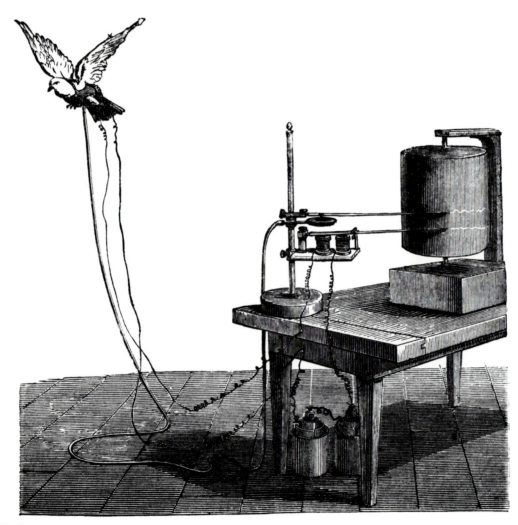

23. Electromagnetic apparatus for the transmission of the wing beats of a
    bird and their inscription on a myograph.

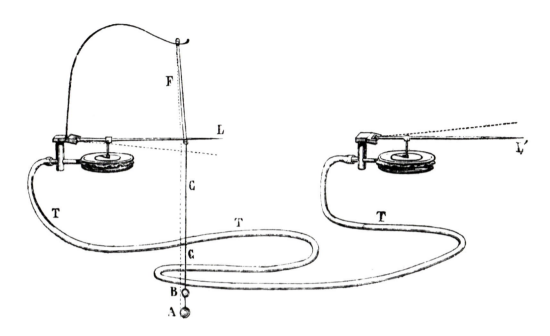

24. Spools with interconnecting levers. Taken from Marey,
Le Vol des oiseaux.

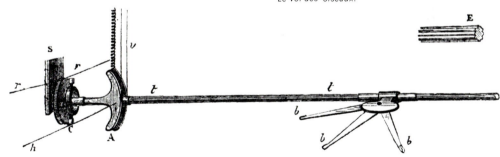

25. Diagram of the pantographic lever for detecting wing movements
and changes in plane. Taken from Marey, *Le Vol des oiseaux*.

Marey would search for other methods. He would even use "converters" made of two levers joined to one another before finding the most economical process, the basic principle of which was this: the system was sensitive to orthogonal translations and these were passed on to a second cylinder connected to it. The horizontal and the vertical were thus added together. Later, Marey would directly capture movement on three axes through a triple rotating joint able to yield to any number of movements, including spiral and helicoidal.

A laborious preparation still had to be gone through. The bird had to be attached not only to enable it to be tracked by limiting its movement but also to lighten the weight: the transmitting apparatus was stable and centrally fixed. The pigeon was "hitched up" to it and sent the three expected "signals" to the contraption. To put it simply, the bird moved within the mega-apparatus instead of having to carry it. Because it was not possible to "miniaturize" the measuring device, Marey inverted the terms and put the bird – without compromising its freedom of motion in the air – into the contraption (using straps that could travel the length of the rails) (figures 26, 27). In sum, despite a few uncertainties, this was progress. Marey had slightly modified yesterday's tools; he had replaced the initial mechanics of transmission with some "optical-electrical" fragments and thus overcome more than one problem.

Whoever wishes to understand Marey should think of him as a clever "detector." Faced with an increasingly elusive and impalpable reality (aerial locomotion), he relentlessly experimented with ways to continue sampling, transferring and projecting onto screens the most minute (infrasensory) modifications. He could later modify them, analyzing and comparing the various "inscriptions" at leisure.

Although I shall not follow all the threads being woven together, I shall come back to some of them – especially in Chapter 3 when I look at the emergence of the third Marey. This does not pretend to be a complete epistemographical study – that has already been

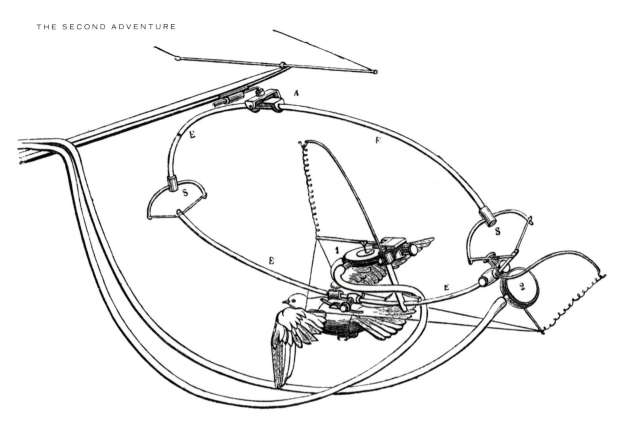

26. Device for harnessing the pigeon to the revolving frame. Taken from
Marey, *Le Vol des oiseaux*.

27. Arrangement of the revolving frame. Taken from Marey, *Le Vol des
oiseaux*.

done well. The aim here is to illuminate the soul of his research, its evolving problematic and constant methodological refinements.

Thus, I have come to the veritable turning point that marks the appearance, according to my thesis (with all the reservations that word implies), of "the second Marey": that is to say, the complete abandon of one method of data collection (mechanical imprints) for another, the optical silhouette. And hence, a new crop of questions, a different world.

Photography, for that is what is in question, had enjoyed widespread development for more than a quarter of a century. It did not appear to be of use, however, because it dealt in snapshots, whereas Marey specialized in "continuous data recordings." What he wanted was *movements*, not moments. For Marey's biogrammatology to benefit from this possibility, three "innovations" (after 1878) were needed. These should not be distinguished between too fully because they arise from the same effort to take the daguerreotype beyond its own limitations. Essentially, there was a converging of three "picture-taking" experts (Eadweard Muybridge, Gaston Tissandier and Jules Janssen), sometimes unknowingly. All three approached the same problem from different directions and would allow Marey (whom they all more or less knew), who was also on the brink, to enter the arena; given the thrust of his earlier work, he was just waiting to enter. This is not "happy coincidence" but a single and inevitable confluence.

Muybridge was a noted professional photographer in San Francisco and follower of Louis Daguerre, of whose inventions and advances he made use. He received an order, from his richest customer, Leland Stanford, former governor of California, railway magnate and breeder of horses, famous for his studs. Stanford knew of Marey's work through *Animal Mechanism* (1873). This seems quite understandable because its conclusions had a direct bearing on the economic sphere, as much in the world of labor as in that of the rational use of motor forces ("live machines"). The great stable owner was quite overcome by Marey's notations,

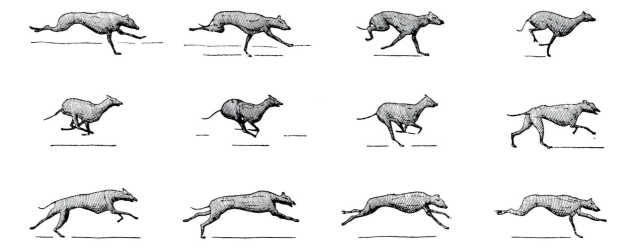

28. Breakdown of the movements of a greyhound racing. Sketch made
from snapshots by Muybridge. Taken from *La Nature* (February 1892).

even if they were basically another version of Vincent's, the racehorse suspended in its gallop with its four hooves in the air. He quite reasonably hoped the photographer could produce detailed information on the way his thoroughbreds ran.

Muybridge the cameraman, talented and not short of material or financial resources, quickly set to work. First, he equipped a track at Palo Alto, site of his patron Stanford's stables. He set up a series of "sensitive plates," initially twelve, then twenty-four, then thirty, each linked to a shutter. The horse (the most purely bred horses were used: Abe Edginton, Mahoruch and especially Occident) ran or galloped and snapped a thin cord stretched across its path producing instant closure of an electrical circuit. A magnet was then activated, momentarily opening the series of lenses. The release, electric or electro-magnetic from batteries, properly synchronized, ensured the celerity of the operation (automatic electric photograph). The black horse's hooves and thrust stood out even more because of a large white screen with vertical stripes (in order to measure the spaces, thus the speeds) parallel to the length of track (the horses were black against a contrast-ing background).

Muybridge broadened his method to include all animals, particularly hunting dogs, stags and greyhounds (figure 28). He would later apply it to humans; specifically to the athlete and medical subjects (in 1884, in collaboration with Francis Xavier Dercum) for the study of ataxia.

I have not engineered this chain of influence: here is an extract from one of Muybridge's letters: "Reading [Marey's] famous work on *Animal Mechanism* inspired Governor Stanford's first thoughts on the possibility of solving the problem of locomotion with the help of photography (30 cameras obscura with electric shutters placed 12 inches from each other)."[22] At first Muybridge obtained twelve shots in half a second, but we will return to a discussion of these results.

Muybridge went to Paris no doubt because his analyses had shaken the physiology and art communities. In fact, at this very moment (December 1878) a scientific journal, *La Nature*, played a major role, as would its founder and editor, Tissandier, a well-known expert in ballooning and daring voyager, a lover of the picturesque and the exotic. It is important to note here the close links between the daguerreotype and air travel, which allowed for wide panoramas, vast landscapes and views of cities seen from the gondola of the balloon, not to mention spying and aid to armies in the field. Félix Nadar had associated the two, as had Tissandier.

A true scientific adventurer and explorer in every sphere, Tissandier wrote several books, including *Les Merveilles de la photographie* (in 1874) and *La Photographie en ballon* (1886). He later wrote the preface for Jacques Ducom's *Débuts d'un amateur photograph* (1894).[23] He started a column called "Photography" in his weekly review, in which spectacular "images" were published along with all the transformations and improvements in cameras.

Tissandier was very much a part of the trend launched by Marey to promote registering devices, which enabled the progress of the experimental sciences. In the years after 1874 (*Les Merveilles de la photographie*), he praised Armand Pouriau for his outstanding work on "recording instruments"; the astrophysicist Warren de la Rue, the undisputed master of astronomical, solar and lunar photography and "reader" of the moon's craters and ridges (beginning in 1859); and Lewis Rutherford, who produced beautiful images of nebulae.

Tissandier, a chemist by training, extolled above all the merits of "chemical fixation," which, in his view, "even indicates speed" and could register the slowest movements.[24] He drew from photography implications for both experimental science and society, claiming, for example (in 1874), that judges might be aided by it in their fight against criminals: "Perhaps the criminal portrait-gallery should be open to the public so that it would be of more service. It would make it easier to arrest offenders whom the police are seeking."[25]

Given the above, it comes as no surprise that Tissandier, fully aware of the work of the new American laboratories, received pictures "of the horse running" from Muybridge himself, which *La Nature* published on December 14, 1878:

> We have received a series of extraordinary photographs from Mr. E. J. L. Muybridge of San Francisco.... They offer the solution to a problem that has long been fruitlessly studied, namely the recapturing of the different moments of the horse's pace as it walks, trots and gallops. There are considerable difficulties in this. Those who have performed snapshot photography will understand the scale of these difficulties and agree that it is a remarkable patience and skill that has made it possible to fix in its different positions the picture of a racehorse travelling at a speed of nearly 20 m a second, that of an express train or a windstorm. It is *La Nature*'s good fortune to be able to publish them for the first time.[26]

I quote at length because the crucial change appears here in black and white. A few days later, on December 18, Marey wrote to his friend Tissandier, who published the correspondence:

> Dear friend, I am delighted with Mr. Muybridge's snapshots which you published in the recent issue of *La Nature*. Could you put me in touch with the author? I would like to ask him to give his assistance to the solution of certain physiological problems which are extremely difficult to solve by other methods. There is the question of bird flight, for example....[27]

The "chemical sensor," then, made its appearance (at the end of 1878). It superseded the electromechanical method at the very moment when the latter had dethroned the purely mechanical. A highly pertinent comment on this, in *La Méthode graphique*, cites the change preceding the upheaval: "If I had to start this kind of experiment again, I would give up air-driven signals and adopt light electrical ones.... Thin conducting wires would fit better along the animal's [horse's] legs than rubber tubes."[28] This repentance came to nothing because, at the end of this same year, 1878, he stopped thinking about refining the graphic method and replaced it.

The America–Europe connection was established and a correspondence begun; nevertheless the problem of locomotion started all over again. Marey did not hide his enthusiasm and acclaimed the San Francisco photographer who had produced the definitive "shot of a racing thoroughbred." But how could he illuminate the flight of birds, of the pigeon or dragonfly? He could not force them to pass before a succession of cameras and apparatuses, nor enclose them between the rails of a track. This preliminary reservation or objection was followed by more serious ones.

After Muybridge and Tissandier, the third protagonist to enter the scene was the astrophysicist Janssen, director of the observatory at Meudon. After a doctoral thesis on the subject of vision, around 1873, he turned, like many at the time, to astronomical photography. He thus undertook a large number of projects: the study of atmospheric rays in the solar spectrum, eclipses of the sun and an account of its spots, and observing the passage of Venus (for the first time, in 1874).

But Janssen was unhappy with the results of celestial optics because the light was so violent that the image captured was flooded and overexposed. It took on dimensions that warped reality; details were often obliterated; or else "artefacts" came into sight. By way of a solution, Janssen thought of shortening exposure time as much as possible while enlarging the diameter of the shot, neither of which, obviously, could be done without the other.

Thus, he invented the "astronomical revolver," which allowed extremely short takes (1/300th of a second). A circular sensitive plate was made to move at regular intervals by a trigger, while in front of it turned a disc pierced with regularly spaced apertures that would

29. Firing position with the photographic gun. Taken from Marey,
    Movement.

determine the "shots." The combination of a high-speed shutter and the sensitivity of gelatine-bromide allowed Janssen, in 1874 in Japan, to shoot the passage of Venus in spite of the double obstacle of intense light and slow movement. To reconstitute the event later, or simply to capture it, he multiplied the number of shots: "When it was nearing the moment of contact [the passage of the planet], I decided to take a series of photographs at very short and regular intervals, in such a way that the photographic image of the contact would necessarily be included in the series and at the same time give the exact moment of the phenomenon."[29] The rapidity and brevity of the shots were compensated by their number.

Janssen used this Mareyan reasoning to replace a visual retinal approach with the chemical plate, provided he could prevent overload from the more radiant areas of the solar disc: "The poor quality of the photographic images obtained until now was due solely to the unfavorable conditions in which they were obtained. Among these circumstances, the most important is overexposure to the sun's rays."[30] Janssen's masterstroke lay in being able to shorten the time of this exposure and making a sensitive, photoastronomical telescope.

Moreover, Janssen called on biologists and all researchers to take up his weapon, the revolver, so as to be able to record rapid vibrations and operational cycles. In the *Bulletin de la Société Française de Photographie* of April 1876, he went as far as raising the possibility of catching the mechanism "of bird flight" as well as other secrets of animal locomotion. This was all Marey needed to follow up Janssen's exhortations: he made his "chrono-photographic gun" (figure 29).

Why this haste? Because Marey glimpsed an end to disappointment, saw the possibility of trapping movements at the rhythm of their own speed. Indeed, the gun turned so rapidly that it could easily take twelve photos per second (1/720th of a second each). The barrel of the gun housed the lens and, behind it, a chamber contained a clock mechanism, which set the apparatus's different elements in motion, including the two discs, the multiple-aperture

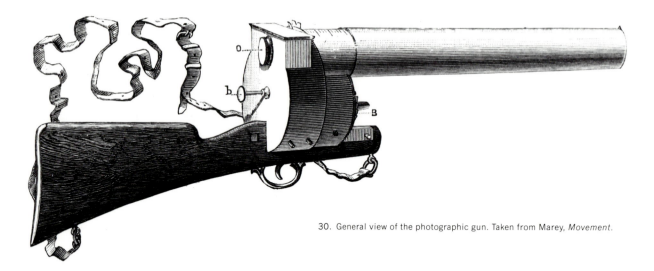

30. General view of the photographic gun. Taken from Marey, *Movement*.

shutter and the chemical plate. This rather sophisticated system had to overcome something of a contradiction: coupling rotation of the two discs but also stopping them for a moment when the light was allowed in, for the duration of the luminous imprint (figures 30, 31).

A "box for hiding" (figure 32) had to be added to house twenty-five sensitive plates "to be transferred to the gun without being exposed to the light."[31] Thus, "the weapon" could be reloaded quickly. Another device "calculated" the times, in such a way that the exposure time was known as well as the intervals between successive images (chronophotography). Soon, Marey would again devote himself to capturing all angles of the bird in flight; from below and above, moving away and approaching. He would be able to observe the inclination of the wing planes, the curve of the primaries and the slightest movements of the body. Needless to say, it would take several years (beginning in 1878–1882) to perfect such an assemblage. I skip ahead to underline the connection between Janssen's "revolver" and Marey's gun.

31. Detail of the optical mechanism in the photographic gun.
Taken from Marey, *Movement*.

32. Mechanism of the "changing box" for housing sensitive plates.
Taken from Marey, *Movement*.

To conclude my narrative of these entanglements, I should point out that Janssen's suggestions preceded Muybridge's successes. The evidence comes from the letter of December 1878, in which Marey congratulated the American photographer on his "shots" of the galloping horse, and already raises the question of aerial locomotion: "For the problem of the flight of birds, I dreamed of a kind of photographic gun...." In April 1882, this dream would become reality.

Let me recapitulate the two stages of my account: in 1878, an image specialist opened the way to chemical fixation, the new sensor. He successfully resolved the question of "running quadrupeds," but was still stumped by flying species (aerial locomotion). In 1874, an astrophysician independently supplied Marey with the technical solution, or at least its principle: the revolver that could be used for any movement that was either beyond his powers of observation or very distant (the stars). It allowed shots at such short intervals that it achieved the successive or sliding quality of phases.

Tissandier facilitated the cross-connections between the two. It was he who introduced Marey to Muybridge's horses and Janssen's celestial views – currents in the fluid photosphere, the movements of the countless solar granulations, which he published. *La Nature* commented on both these cinematographies. Three experts in "optical acquisition," then, led Marey forward, promoting his development and inspiring a method (electrophotography), a solution (the revolver), and a new area of conquest (the ultra-inaccessible, the very slow and especially the very fast).

———————————

It might seem that the problem was now settled, that Marey's goal had been simply to tie these strands together. In fact, it would take several years and new findings for Marey to be able to achieve satisfactory results. He was uniquely good at extending rudimentary tests and pushing them beyond their limits. His genius lies in subtle improvements and a meticulous tinkering that would obtain better performance from his instruments.

During this period (1878–1882), he would find and champion three technical changes to the optical process that would make it fully operational. What was recorded had to be exact and clear, otherwise reading it – which was as fundamental as recording it – would remain a problem. A preliminary obstacle had to be negotiated. It was as much a battle against time as against space, but the first could not be conquered without mastery of the second.

Muybridge's work ultimately only gave the illusion of cinematics. What he captured with his twelve cameras – he would eventually have thirty lined along the track – were phases of movement that he had arbitrarily divided into sections, which he would subsequently have to reassemble as best he could (figure 33).

The chronophotographic gun – the first portable camera – was equipped with a single

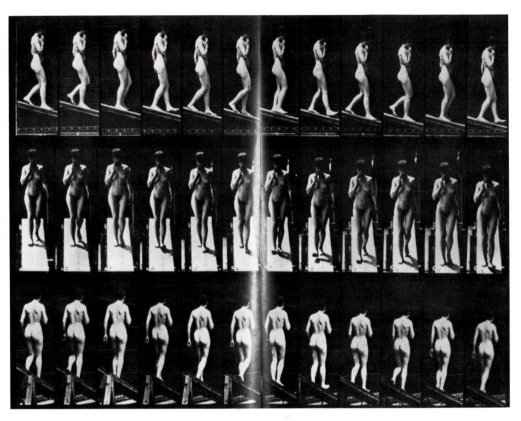

33. Woman with one hand at her mouth descending an inclined plane.
Taken from Muybridge, *The Human Figure in Motion*, pl. 110.

rotating disc, thus making it possible to take pictures of the flying bird throughout its course. The difference is obvious: a single, moving plate instead of twelve or thirty.

Subsequent operations would attempt to get closer to spatial movement in order truly to coincide with it. The obstacles presented by the materials, indeed the heaviness of the whole instrument – the weight of the glass plate, the slowness of the shutter and the rotations that slowed down its reactions still more – had to be overcome so as to capture "the intermediate positions" between states.

The first of Marey's three "clever ideas" was as follows: Suppose that "the sensitive receiver" had picked up a suddenly illuminated body (a bird, for example). This glint only took up part of the receiving area; one or more images could be recorded on what was left (the area not yet imprinted), until the whole of this "sensitive mirror" was full. What Marey attempted, then, in July 1882, when he started working on the new method, was to have the swirling of the wings and that of parallel fluttering images coincide; or, as he put it, to synchronize "the aperture-disc's revolutions and those of the wing."[32] This reduced "dead time" and assured the relative motionlessness of a momentarily still receiver. To establish this synchronization between the model and its trace, a rather vast "dark field" was needed. This was the station; its walls coated in lamp-black, the floor with bitumen, and wide strips of dark velvet in every corner so that the surroundings (thus eliminated) could not interfere with what was to be captured: the bird's wings or the horse's hooves. Marey's process was an innovation not only because he used a single camera – a perfected version of Janssen's revolver – but also because a single disc could capture successive spatial movements (or several poses in the same place) by itself. In short, linking the shot more closely to the subject kept it from being diluted (figure 34).

This was a definite shift from Muybridge and Janssen. It was surprising to hear philosophers – Bergsonian – who insisted that time was "ungraspable," pouring inexorably between

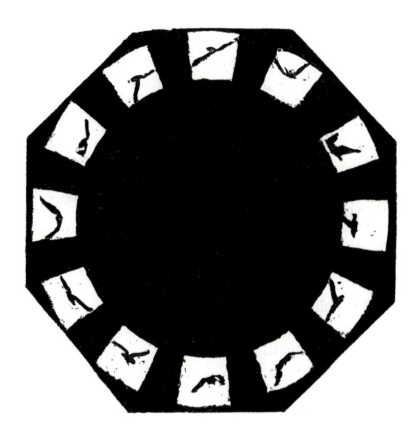

34. Plate from the photographic gun with twelve views of a gull in flight.
Taken from Marey, *Movement*.

our fingers, and who therefore dismissed a technique they considered powerless against it – repeat the same thing in regard to kinetics: it was elusive; speed could not be housed on or in the motionless. Yet, at this same time, it was the (relative) "fixity" of what was being imprinted that made its capture possible. It was a paradox that the more the support "dwelled" on movement, the better it could reproduce it. Marey's idea, however, had worked so well that it was difficult to distinguish fully between the different phases of movement, which dissolved into one another (a dense, homogenized whole). Images of transition were certainly part of the goal, but so were "points of reference," which would reveal the "stages of transition" and the style of movement. Too much continuity dissolved and absorbed into a single sequence what came in jerks. Triumph almost turned to failure: it was necessary to capture protrusions, linkages and multiple phases (or the discontinuity of continuity itself).

Camera and technique had to find a place between fusion and fragmentation. It was thus necessary both to "sample" precisely and to "contract" slightly: a certain amount of distancing seemed helpful. The momentarily "still" plate seemed designed to answer the problem (figure 35). It might be said in passing that movement connects segments as well as certain excesses that quickly cancel each other out (soaring and falling, springing and releasing). Late Bergsonism put aside rhythm to concentrate on the final melodic curve or result: the final form. It held as homogeneous that which was seen, yet should appear heterogeneous (a combination of harmonics). Insofar as it had long upheld and proclaimed the reverse, this was like censure.[33]

The successful process of the momentarily still plate was accompanied by many other precautions. Marey soon began to use a broad sensitive surface as well as a shutter of more than a meter in diameter. This was because the effects of diffraction altered and blurred the snapshot, making it a silhouette instead of a "view." The apertures being used were too

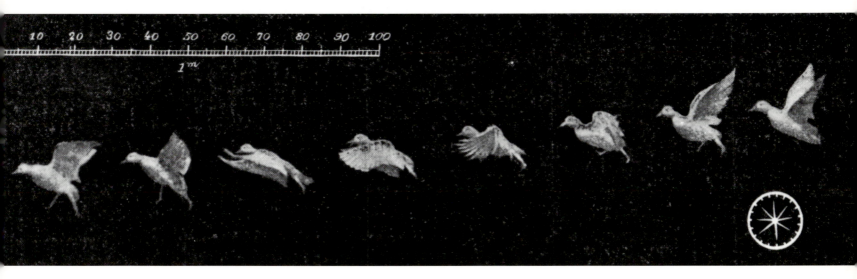

35. The flight of the duck with the successive positions of its wings at
    intervals of 1/10 second. Chronophotograph on a fixed plate. Taken
    from Marey, "Nouveaux développements de la chronophotographie."

narrow or else beveled. It was more effective to enlarge the slits of a disc of imposing dimensions, which could also be turned more rapidly. The flux of light entered more easily, producing better results. The little trolley – the famous black box on wheels that Marey designed for his chronophotographic station in the Parc des Princes – was inspired by this new development. It was an important modification because the short duration of a shot had to be accompanied by a significant amount of light.

Marey's second idea was what he called "partial photography."[34] In the first period of "mechanical acquisition," Marey had already attempted to resolve the problem of speeding up tracings that were too slow or elongated, and conversely reducing those that were too fast or large. The datum had to fit the size of the piece of paper. His cameras were able, and indeed obliged, to impose rates and proportions.

I have established that the speed attained would tend to produce superimposition and dovetailing of data. Progress had gone almost too far. There had to be a way of limiting the frenetic confusion without losing the essential: velocity. But how? Braking a running horse or slowing the beating of a pigeon's wings were hardly options.

What was Marey's response? What were his experimental inclinations? What did he do when presented with a host of complex and insurmountable problems, such as increasingly complicated instruments with too many correctives, or curves blending and printing on top of each other? He changed direction: he attacked the model and vice versa. The earlier construction of a contraption that at once imprisoned and freed a bird obeyed the same dialectic: adapting to an unstable "median" situation.

In this case, the camera, painstakingly adapted for its delicate task, was not altered; only the animal or other subject could be modified. Here, "stripes" were used: the horse, bird or human subject was coated or clothed from head to foot in black except for a few thin streaks of shiny metal, or little dots of white paper stuck to appropriate areas (figures 36, 37).

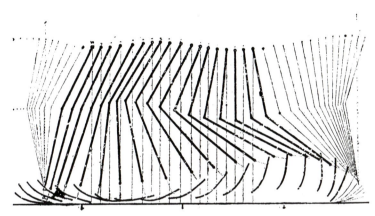

36. Subject wearing black outfit with white lines and points. Taken from Marey, *Movement*.

37. Oscillations of the leg during running: geometric chronophotography. Taken from Marey, *Movement*.

The shot was reduced, the animal stripped of all unnecessaries, optically speaking. And, instead of volume, lines were photographed.

There was an immediate benefit: "Partial photographs are useful because the poses can be greatly multiplied.... This arrangement easily increases tenfold the number of images captured in a given time on the same plate; instead of ten photographs per second, one can take a hundred."[35] Stripes and zones were an ingenious response, offering a number of advantages at once: "not enough" was a disappointment, failing to produce the dynamics of the movement; while "too much" fused it together. However, cutting up into strips, the "much too much" approach, offered sections and transitions at the same time.

Other tricks were involved. A track was painted with light crosswise bands alternating with wide black areas. These divisions helped locate, measure and assess distance traveled and speed, since the time taken was known (chronobiology). The results demanded to be seen: dazzling abstract films showing lines rising and falling back over, then rising and falling again, while at the same time pressing up against each other (figure 38).

It might be argued that such tactics were no advance at all, because a horse, much less a bird, could not be totally covered, like the fencer or the cyclist, in a striped or checkered shell (carapace). There was no problem, however, sticking identifiable pieces of paper (tiny circles, squares and triangles) on them – even to the edges of a wing. The plate recorded the subsequent quivering of these signal points, and they were easily connected later with hand-drawn lines. The whole that had initially been methodically cut up was reassembled. Thus, what was called partial photography was only partial in relation to the moment of "transition" or transfer. Simplification led to a better reconstruction, and nothing was lost.

Marey's was not an outright victory. First, his technique was limited to certain movements, basically those that took place on land. The method could not be applied to fish, which presented a challenge. They continually changed position and place in their tanks,

38. Horse walking, with white markers, around 1886-1887.

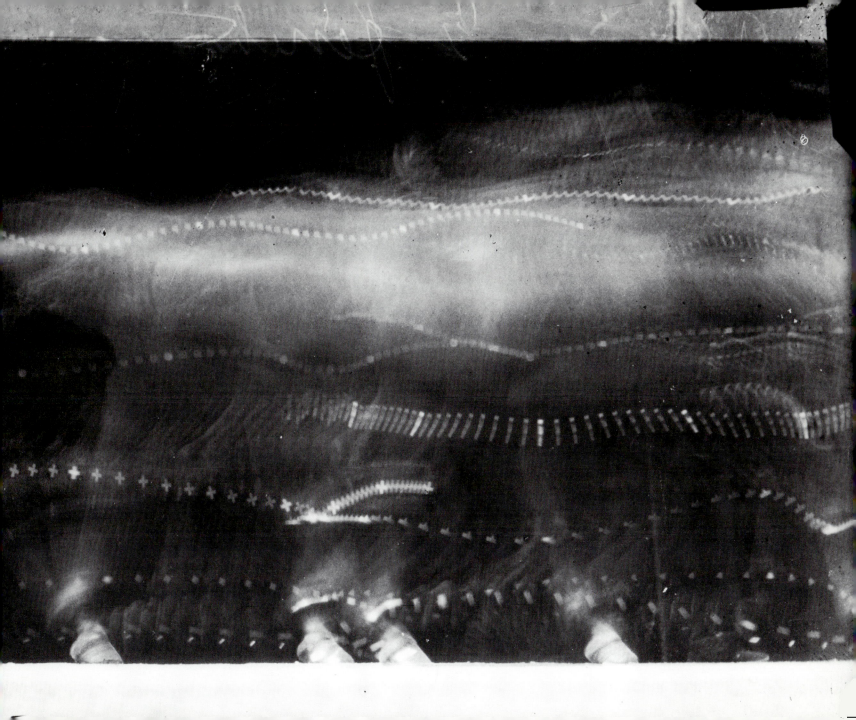

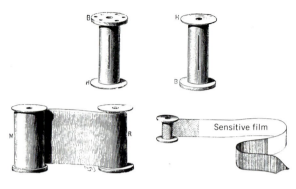

Sensitive film

39. Arrangement of the two metal bobbins employed to wind the light sensitive film. Taken from Marey, *Movement*.

and the layer of water separating them from the lens absorbed a significant amount of light. In addition to the resulting "muddiness," refraction-distortion gave their image a certain sameness. Second, animals had to parade around the narrow confines of a dark shed, which severely limited the shots. He had to wait for birds to arrive, and the rebellious aquatic life escaped completely.

The Mareyan principle was: learn how to let go of an instrument that is too limited or unreliable; "the sensors" have to be improved. Between 1880 and 1890, this is what he would do. Photography-related chemistry was evolving so fast that it allowed him to replace the glass plate, which was, ultimately, a hindrance, with a strip of moveable paper (October 1888); and then a film on a bobbin (1891), which George Eastman of Rochester, New York would later use.

Marey abandoned the system of a momentarily still film plate that had to be loaded, because the darkness it required was too much of a constraint. The bobbin that rolled up the film was flexible yet steady; it was light, with no resistance; slim yet solid. It moved quickly and had a superior recording capacity, and essentially constituted a "black box of images." Everything was miniaturized and it was now possible to target soaring birds or fish darting through the water against a light background: "The object which the camera is taking pictures of may be placed at any distance and in all kinds of lighting conditions. It seemed to me that one of the newest areas to explore was water locomotion (fish, crustaceans and radiata)."[36]

The celluloid ribbon set the photographer free; it lightened the instrument considerably. The discovery of accelerating substances reduced exposure time to nothing (including calotype paper coated with silver gallo-nitrate), which further contributed to the transformation. Two major problems, however, hindered the use of this revolutionary moveable film: The first problem was putting the film into the box and taking it out again without daylight (in which the work was done) affecting it. This was fairly easily and quickly resolved. All that had to be done was to provide a neutral area at one end of the long roll with no emulsion. The part remaining inside the bobbin or magazine was wound gradually onto the second bobbin only after the camera had been closed again. The paper was thus handled and loaded safely. Marey had thought of this process in 1891 (Eastman took it up in 1892) (figure 39). Moreover, this was a time when portable cameras were multiplying and being perfected (such as those of Enjalbert and Fetter, 1885–1886).

The second problem, however, could not really be resolved. It was essential to move the imprinted surface constantly to replace it for a new "shot." The film underwent two contrary movements: a dragging away and a stopping, during the brief moment of a shot. It was essentially the old, ongoing and formidable problem of synchronization and the automatic coupling of two contradictory operations. How could they be combined and linked?

Marey first used an electromagnetic system inspired by telegraphy. A kind of small steel jaw was set in motion by a magnet producing a continuous series of thrusts and withdrawals. It gripped the roll for a fraction of a second, immobilizing, then releasing it so that its continuous movement, temporarily suspended, could carry on. This somewhat abrupt method of "fixation," however, did not seem suitable. Because the grip was too tight while the film was still being pushed, there was a sort of clogging; the strip moved on again with a distinct jerk. Restraint had to be both distinct and faint so as not to hinder or accelerate the movement. Thus, Marey preferred a mechanical "stop" to an electrical grip. This small, flexible, steel strip, capable of stiffening and slackening, was a more supple mechanism: "After the brief halt corresponding to a shot, the bent spring slackens and the strip moves on...."

A make-shift solution, however, was not a real solution; there was nothing to guarantee the equidistance of the images, or the absolute regularity of the movement in the film ribbon. Marey could, nevertheless, leave the station and capture what had eluded him up until then – both the minute (insects) and the unmovable (fish).

There were three adjustments between 1882 and 1890: the temporarily still plate, the provisionally partial image and the regularly moving ribbon. Marey was thus continually improving his new recorder, the optical device, and tackling the most complex movement: the eel's swimming, the echinoderm's flexuosity, the jellyfish's filaments and the hundred-armed polyp's simultaneous raising, withdrawing and retracting of its arms. He delved deeper into the imperceptible and multiple, a long way now from the trotting horse and bird in flight.

I have not yet finished this examination; I must consider the last, most decisive and perhaps most original act. The second Marey (who turned to external movements, which were more mysterious than internal ones, and who changed his recording devices) did not forget the methodological principles established by the first. The three most important were:

1. The need to banish speculation about the vital principle so that only reliable, detailed mechanical solutions would be offered. Thus one of several pronouncements: "I do not

know what the vital phenomena are; I recognize only two kinds of manifestations of life: those that are intelligible to us, which are all of a physical or chemical order, and those that are not. In the latter case, it is better to admit our ignorance than to dress it up in pretended explanations."[37]

2. The second principle was to reassemble a function after it had first been recorded and broken down; only "synthesis" could validate the acquired data of analysis. Marey clearly modeled biomechanics on Marcellin Berthelot's "organic chemistry," and demanded complete reproduction as a means of demonstrating his claims. The first Marey upheld the principle: the movements and noises of the heart were reproduced by pumps and valves, arteries by rubber tubes and lungs by moveable bellows; in short, moving prosthetic equivalents.

It also must be said that the nineteenth century was producing increasingly complex communication devices. Marey witnessed Bréguet's telegraph, the chronometric counters and cogged wheel of Félix Savart, a doctor also interested in vibroscopic phenomena, and many others who favored this new method of conceiving of the living. The second principle had an immediate consequence: investigating the locomotion of birds, pigeons and sea gulls raised aeromotor and ballistic questions and thus the need to build a corresponding "flying machine." What really happened? Did Marey's innovations open the new chapter on aviation?

3. The final principle was that the curves, whether obtained through continuous recording (according to the threefold model of receiver, transmitter and recorder) or chrono-photography (the second period), condensed phenomena, offering the simultaneous as well as the divergent and imperceptible. As his *La Méthode graphique* confirms, this was a sort of contraction or shorthand: "The inscribing apparatuses simplify a great deal...."[38] They extracted the truth from where it was embedded. Similar remarks are made throughout the

book, but calculation was what could and should complete the account. In general, in Marey's view, it was used too soon and produced false results. Watt had led the way with his famous diagram demonstrating, more or less directly, the output of the steam engine, which greatly facilitated numerical evaluation. Tracings were simply a necessary stage. Thus, after the study of bird flight, an understanding of their physical and dynamic exploits would require further developments.

These three principles, in a sense, come down to a single approach; it remains for us to consider how they were put into practice. What did Marey invent in the beginning stages of aeronautics? Surprisingly, most accounts of the history of human aerial locomotion generally ignore him, and this brings me to the core of the problem presented by his biomechanics: his presence in and effect on the elaboration of the modern world. Did he open doors? Was he, directly or not, among those who revolutionized transportation? For now, let us simply ask: Did his research on bird flight make possible the construction and propulsion of airplanes?

I believe that it did and would like to put forward evidence and give Marey due credit for his contribution. Most would agree, a priori, on his involvement (all the more praiseworthy in that the flight of something "heavier than air" still seemed illusory in 1890) if it is true that, for Marey, aerial movement obeyed in principle a simple rapport of forces; and moreover that he had to, and did, construct a "flying machine" or at least worked on one.

At the time, inventions relating to air travel were being hindered or put into question altogether either by parallel developments or by specious considerations. There was the success of the "ballooners," the rise of the "light," Joseph and Jacques Montgolfier's balloon. Balloons were especially successful when hydrogen aided ascent without making them more difficult to steer.

Less successful was the excessive focus on ornithological models, which proved a fruitless detour. It is here that we can place the first of Marey's contributions: he ignored the bird as such and revealed its "mechanics" without continued reference to it as a whole. This was no doubt due to the "science of the image" that was able to produce separation, extract the essential, release a principle from what was obscuring it, and externalize it so as to imitate it ultimately. Marey was not the first, but he nevertheless reinforced the trend and gave it more focus.

Incontestably, all the early pioneers took this route, closely observing the flight of vultures, eagles and large sea birds. Among them were Louis Mouillard and his *The Empire of the Air: An Ornithological Essay on the Flight of Birds* (1881); Otto Lilienthal, with his *Birdflight as the Basis of Aviation* (1889) (not mentioned by Marey); and Alphonse Pénaud, with his *L'Aéronaute* (1873), who was also passionately interested in how birds' wings beat.[39] Pénaud is also to be credited with an interesting discovery. In his quest to solve the mystery of flight, he had noticed that, on occasion, dust particles lit up by the sun would give a graphic picture of the disturbance of the air around birds. For lack of this spontaneous indirect lighting, he used jets of smoke to determine the currents' direction, if not their speed (a graphometry). Experts on the early airplanes (Mouillard, Lilienthal, Pénaud) thus watched sea birds and hawks, hoping to understand their cinematics. However, without enough sophisticated equipment, they sometimes attributed actions to them that they never actually performed and missed ones they did.

Another expert in animal mechanics, James Bell Pettigrew, published *Animal Locomotion: Or Walking, Swimming and Flying, with a Dissertation on Aeronautics* (a very Mareyan title) in 1873. It was a collection of earlier articles in which he developed a thesis as inaccurate as it was seductive: "The wing of the bird does not materially differ from the extremity of the biped or the tail of the fish. It is constructed on a similar plan, and acts on the same principle. The tail of the fish, the wing of the bird, and the extremity of the biped and quadruped are propellers, both structurally and functionally.... In either case the bones are twisted upon themselves like an auger."[40] Revolving became the key to propulsion: helix-wings would be like screws. Marey's response was immediate and scathing: "We do not feel the need to refute such a theory," he wrote in *Animal Mechanism*.[41] He served notice of its rejection by never referring to it again.

He distrusted general and abstract explanations; he first wanted to distinguish between the many varieties of navigation (hovering, gliding, "rowing" with the wings, soaring – the simple slide forward due to acquired speed, counterbalancing the effect of weight, which Marey quickly copied using a piece of paper folded into an obtuse dihedral angle). He made a clear distinction between the various positions in all phases of action: beginning, middle and end. Everything changed constantly; and the wings played several roles. Myography as well as the newer chronophotography (1882–1888) would triumph in the new book of 1890, *Le Vol des oiseaux* (figures 40, 41, 42, 43, 44).

All in all, this three-dimensional optical registering was thoroughly comprehensive and produced two series of results that would lead directly to the "flying automobile":

1. Air served as a fulcrum, which the two wings struck and pushed backward, necessarily producing a lift upward and forward. This came as no surprise. But the recording of both the action of the wing muscles and the movement of the bird's body (by two corroborating methods – Marey always verified a new method through an earlier, obsolete one) also proved that there was a double ascent linked to the wings' revolutions. The more distinct one corresponded to their lowering, the second and smaller to their lifting upward, causing a slowing in speed. Again, few would find this surprising. Lift took place while the wings were lowering.

2. Particularly important was that calculation could now be applied to the graphic results to make them more precise. The forces acting on the bird's body would be measured along with the air's resistance, which increased with the bird's movement. In the case of

40. The flight of the seagull, 1886.

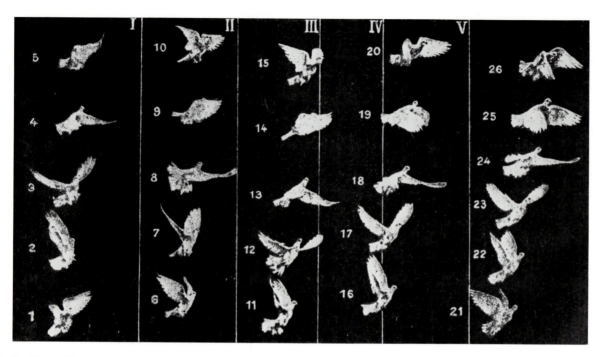

41. Breakdown of the movements of a pigeon in flight. Taken from Marey,
Le Vol des oiseaux.

42. The flight of the seagull, 1886.

43. The flight of the pelican, 1886.

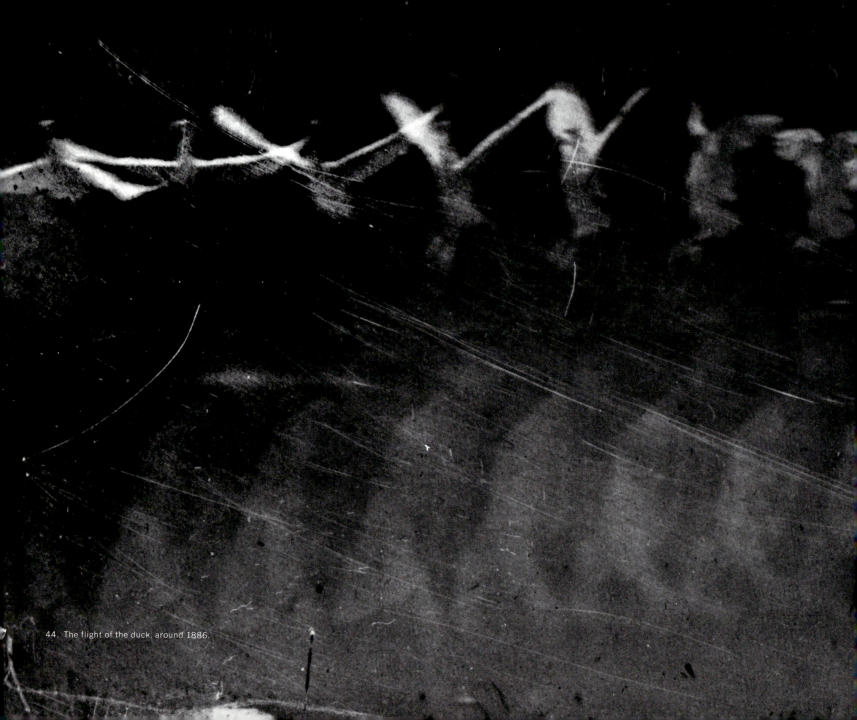

44. The flight of the duck, around 1886.

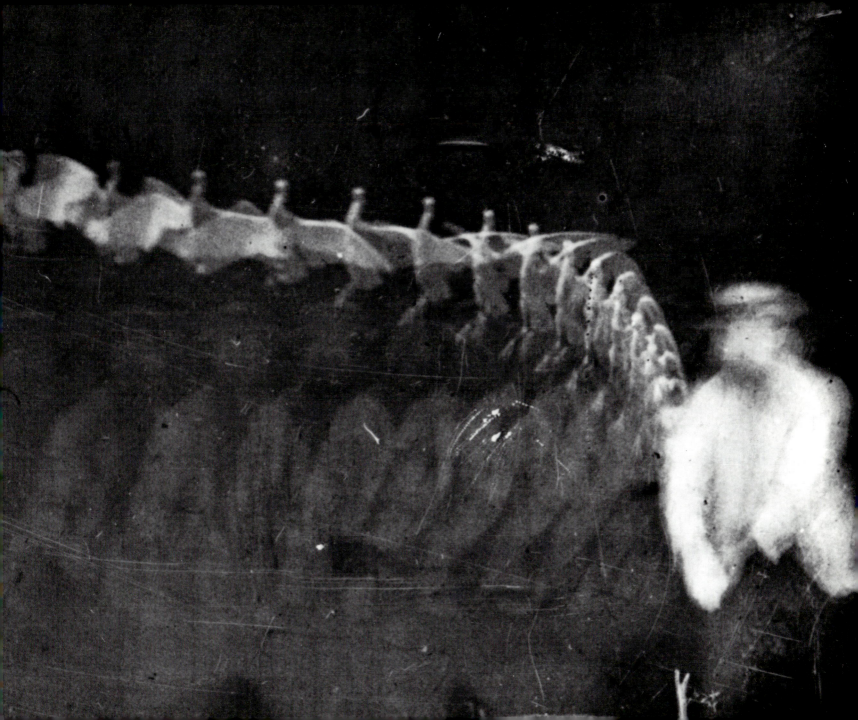

the second measurement, Marey was not, of course, without resources (manometry): "I have done," he wrote, "a long series of experiments to measure the air-pressure at different points of the front and back surfaces of a disc whose speeds have been determined...."[42] But the first measurement was even easier for him (flight through the rowing of the wings, as with migratory birds): the mass (weight) was known, as was the speed of the launched body and its acceleration (the difference between two consecutive moments); even the living projectile had been clearly made visual (ballistics). It was rather obvious that the weight was necessarily and continually neutralized by the push upward. The two factors were linked to good effect: the general formula $R = kSV^2$ offers an outline of it (R being the resistance to be overcome; S the surface of the section of the body pointing in the direction of motion; V the speed; and lastly k, a specific element partly dependent on weight). This was complicated by other aspects: the center of gravity was constantly shifting; one wing might beat faster than the other and so on.

However, most significant is how much Marey's theory had evolved. *Animal Mechanism*, of 1873, was limited to a laborious description of the pigeon's movements (the mechanical sensor, transmission through air tubes, the revolving frame). In 1890, however, in *Le Vol des oiseaux*, Marey went much further, precisely measuring all the forces present. He was making his approach more mechanical. The second stage of graphic science was indeed possible only because the first had been totally mastered (photographing successive positions, assessing distances covered). *Animal Mechanism* was perfectly aware of its own incompletion:

> As for measuring the work expended in flight, we must, before we can undertake it, have a perfect knowledge of the resistance which the air presents to surfaces of every form.... We only know as yet the movements of the wings; the resistance which they encounter in the air has yet to be determined. Our experiments on this subject are in progress.[43]

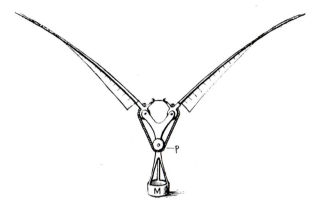

45. Apparatus for the imitation of the wing beat of a bird. Taken from
Marey, *Le Vol des oiseaux.*

It was also significant that Marey moved from an ornithopteral understanding (figure 45) (the beating wings of his artificial bird, up and down and forward and backward) to abandoning the notion of similarity in favor of the airplane (mono- or biplane, slightly inclined, with motorized propellers), without disregarding the importance of other morphological factors.

The technological realization was, in fact, entrusted to Victor Tatin who worked in Marey's laboratory. He published three articles in *Physiologie expérimentale: Travaux du laboratoire Marey*: "Expériences sur le vol mécanique" (1876); "Recherches synthétiques sur le vol" (1877), and "Sur le mécanisme du vol" (1878–1879). Around 1879, he built a (small-scale) plane in which the fuselage served as a tank for compressed air, which could activate a motor connected to two tractor-propellers (positioned in front). This was a departure from Pénaud, who used wound-up strips of rubber as the motor force (his light planophore dates from 1871).

Marey's research directly inspired Tatin, as he was fond of pointing out, first because he established that it was not the bird, but its flight that was to be "copied," but particularly because he began to pose the problem in increasingly aerodynamic terms. Marey discovered and then demonstrated that flying creatures had solved the problem with great economy: the energy expended did not exceed that which the simplest machine could supply; humans ought to be able to do as well. *Animal Mechanism* ended with this sentence: "Mechanism can always reproduce a movement, the nature of which has been clearly defined."

Tatin was preceded by the Englishmen George Caylay and William Henson. They had already solved problems of construction and advocated "fixed wings" as well as a system of propulsion using propellers. Indeed, the essentials had been found before Marey: Caylay had already made a model of a glider and Henson had obtained a patent for his flying machine. But Tatin's aerial and Mareyan "automobile," which used compressed air, nevertheless marked a step forward in the process, entering the whirlwind of trials and triumphs that characterized the end of the nineteenth century. This small-scale model, with its powerful motor (figure 46), validated hypotheses of the kind associated with Giovanni Borelli (praised by Marey, he was no doubt the first to establish a purely mechanical concept in his treatise *De motu animalium* [1680][44]). The model flew for several minutes inside its revolving frame, as it was still held by a rope to a post, like a kite. Though not revolutionary, it was nevertheless a moment in, and testimony to, the evolution in progress. Marey and Tatin's aerodynamics deserves its place in the adventure of the conquest of the air (navigation). It contributed to the eclipse of the reign of "aerostats" (balloons) and began to transform man, not into a bird (the old dream or myth) but into a motorist of the sky.

Is this to overrate or glorify Marey? Am I overestimating his achievements? *Animal Mechanism* contained an avowal that revealed the motives and aims explicitly pursued by Marey:

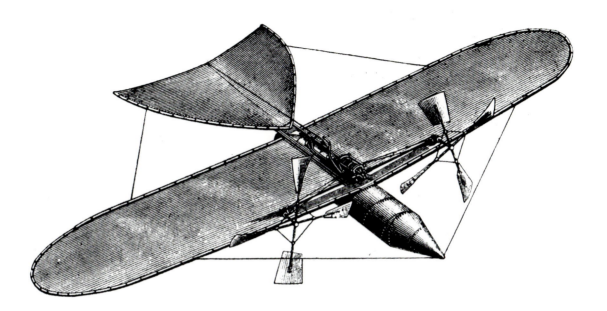

46. Perspective view of the "automobile" driven by compressed air. Taken
from Victor Tatin, *Eléments d'aviation*.

We do not hesitate to admit that what has sustained us in this laborious analysis of the different acts in the flight of the bird, has been the steady hope of being able to imitate, less and less imperfectly, this admirable type of aerial locomotion. Our attempts, which have been interrupted during the last two years, have already met with some success.[45]

This quotation illuminates Marey's approach, which continually moved from ornithological copy to a purely physical-mathematical solution. We should note also that he was in the best position to relaunch aerial research: those who did not look closely enough at the natural flight of birds (which are heavier than air) would fail; those who took "too biological" an approach would lose their way.

Marey avoided this double impasse in his work and spirit alike: he had always sought to ravish physiology's workings and secrets so as to transpose them into an artificial schema of equivalent construction. It has to be said, then, that he, above all others, possessed the means to slip between the problems and assist the development of the "new transport systems" of the air. He helped construct "a thing very close to a bird," that was nevertheless different from it.

I have said that a third Marey would emerge, and it is about this time that he began to appear. From 1890 to 1904 (the year he died) he often moved away from neurobiology (although not entirely; he would study positions and gestures and movements of falling, as striking as that of the cat that always lands on its feet) to study purely physical "subjects," including hydrodynamics, eddies and waves in water, the vast area of rheology and the disturbances caused by obstacles. Whereas before the fish in water was examined and photographed, henceforth water alone was examined, without the creatures living and moving in it. Water and air, as well as the plane (in short, the *animal without the animal*), facilitated the transition.

After studying internal organic movement, Marey took into account the external (using new photoelectric sensors), until finally tackling movements in which the bearer or guide had disappeared. Again, having succeeded in recording the tiniest and innermost tremors, Marey followed his own progressive logic and soon penetrated the domain of the wholly invisible and extraordinary; an environment or universe without object (or subject).

His approach obliged him to employ methods that would render perceptible that which was thought "optically empty." A wave, for example, would be made to go through a sluice or narrowed canal. The narrowing created a current or, failing that, a slowing down; or again, "A solid cylinder is plunged into the water, at regular and easily measured intervals. The cylinder's regular oscillations make a pattern in the liquid. These rhythmic impulses should be produced in the part of the canal away from where the movement is to be examined."[46] Then, methods of detecting the swelling and splashing of the current could be put into effect.

Going further, Marey sought to discover what happened within, to discover the currents themselves, the thin streams inflecting and dividing. In the middle of a liquid mass, he placed solid forms of various shapes (round, parallelepiped, fish-shaped) all made of glass so that light could pass through them. He designed a kind of microdramaturgy to interrupt continuity. In addition, the movements "are made visible by means of small shiny bodies suspended in the water which are lit up by sunlight" (he first took wax and resin and then silvered the resulting pearls; they were denser than water and went to the bottom extremely slowly). This meant that it became possible to photograph flows, trails and deflected trajectories. A similar study was conducted with air (figure 47). Instead of the cylinder to stir up water, a machine whirled smoke onto various surfaces; eddies were then

 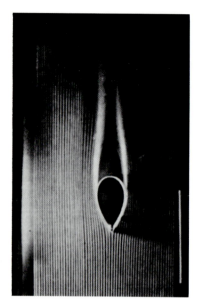 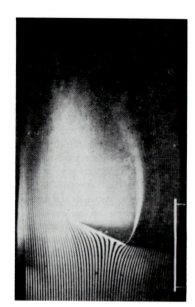

47. Chronophotographic studies of air movements (smoke trails) created around obstacles of various shapes. Taken from *La Nature* (September 1901).

described by the projected particles. A magnesium light enabled the swirls to be recorded as they widened, pulled back, curled and so forth. To measure the speed of these "tracers," the tubes producing them were shaken. These lateral, multiple shocks provoked undulations that spread from top to bottom throughout. Their progress was easily followed, the stroboscopic effect could be graduated and "marks" could be inscribed in or on it. An electric vibrator (set at ten vibrations per second) also created many different patterns. The tests and materials were varied. A liquid or gas could be colored; Marey would then introduce it into a container filled with the same colorless material. A permeation or slow expansion of one into the other took place, the same penetrating the same. Marey's followers (specifically Lucien Bull) pointed to the parallel efforts of James Maxwell who used iron filings to make visible the lines of force of a magnetic field (diagram).

It seems then that, at the end of his scientific life, Marey's pace showed no sign of slackening, while his interests widened. He gained access to movements that had neither bearer nor motor, that were artificial, unknown, bizarre and more imperceptible than ever. He was producing as much as "reproducing" movement.

Movement, Marey's most synoptic and fundamental work, no doubt because written last, took a definite turn in this direction. Chapter 17 is entitled "Microscopic Chronophotography." It is concerned less with the vibrating cilia or flexuous stems of vorticellae than the crystallization of certain salts — the slow passage of liquid into solid. The same work also describes the pure play of fine lines (straight, curved, oblique), all turning and intersecting, which created surfaces and volumes before our eyes. The biological is left aside. The lines also might be replaced by different colored bands or metal strips: "At issue is an imaginary form, which finds no counterpart in nature. Such imaginary forms are stranger still, when, instead of matte substances being employed in their construction, a polished material is used which reflects the sun's rays from certain points of its surface."[47]

Experimental work took a playful turn. Marey drew closer to what he had attempted earlier (especially in *La Méthode graphique*) in the wake of Wheatstone and Lissajous: the capturing of multiple vibrations, the combinations of their twists and turns. However, he now increased the number of cameramen and proposed a more exhaustive as well as more deliberately abstract cinematography.

No beating hearts, no contracting muscles, no running horses and no flying birds: little by little Marey was entering, *volens nolens*, into a kind of Vasarely-esque aesthetic; the genesis of strange figures and landscapes. It was no longer a matter of fragments of air or a vortex of water; the things themselves were no longer distinguishable. He was ushering in a spectacle of fissure and turbulence. Marey, so attentive to reality and scrupulously detailed realism, ended up, paradoxically, with freeform graphics and "formalism." But now I am approaching "the third Marey."

48. Chronophotograph of a jump
from a chair, 1884.

Repercussions and the Culture Industry

Was Marey, as I believe, the artisan of the modern world? And if so, in what way? The question already has been touched on in relation to bird flight and its reproduction (Chapter 2), where Marey was an innovator because his knowledge in biology helped him transgress the biological, and when, as mentioned earlier, Marey's photography finally reached the subject of pure hydro- and aerodynamic forces, a kind of logic of shapes and combinations explicitly aimed at throwing light on the relations between a number of colliding elements (figure 48).

Traces of this aesthetic and constructional morphology are found in the work of a precursor of Marey, Leonardo da Vinci, who was likewise a passionate enthusiast of machines, movement, running and flight. Distinct echoes also can be heard in Paul Valéry, whose work was very Mareyan. In fact, he blended Leonardo and Marey together: "He molds the water round a swimmer," he wrote in regard to Leonardo, "into clinging scarves, draperies that show the effort of muscles in relief. As for the air, he transfixes it in the wake of soaring larks as ravelings of shadow; it is pictured in the frothy flights of bubbles...."[1] Valéry adds: "His precise *imagination* creates the sort of effects that photography has since revealed as fact."[2]

As will be seen, Marey the physiologist – sometimes unknowingly – entered the sciences of art, communications and culture, where not surprisingly he quickly stirred up controversy. The man who had used science to create images of the most complex and obscure data (with systems of inscription that were first mechanical, then electro-optical), inevitably collided with, disturbed and mobilized those working in representation (the plastic arts). With and through Marey, art would indeed experience some real upheavals (our "third Marey").

First, however, why did I write "unknowingly"? Two rather related reasons justify this:

1. The man who, from the beginning, had ruled out the sensory, brought an unknown universe out of the shadows. In his view, we were too content with "seeing"; we had to go beyond this screen, escape the prison of the retina. As is well known, the Surrealists and their sympathizers had been receptive to explorations that recalled Freud's. He discovered the unconscious and its many chasms, but Marey, at the same time, was setting foot on a different continent – the neuromotor – made of rhythms, muffled pulses and fluxes traversing the corporeal machine (producing nervous discharges, reactions; in short, the automatic writing of nature itself).

What Marey produced was more than radiography, which showed the striking and baroque image of a skeleton beneath the living creature. He revealed structures that were buried yet mobile: a construction full of springs. More important still was a simple trick that filmmakers were to use, the aims of which have already been discussed. It consisted of dressing the person-mannequin entirely in black, including a black hood (only a few key lines being emphasized by a thin white stripe or something sparkling). This produced a veritable working drawing of movement, a phantasmagoria that was inevitably impressive, even staggering; one could see a series of sloping marks, overlapping and running into each other. How could anyone fail to be astounded by the athlete-subject metamorphosed into a flight of lines? (See figures 49, 50.) Does not all metamorphosis, regardless, open the door to the unexpected, if not to dreams?

2. In addition, Marey's best-known work, his recordings, occupied a position between science and art, caught in this odd double obligation.

49. Chronophotograph of a jump from a standing still position, around 1882.

50. Geometric chronophotograph of a running jump, 1883.

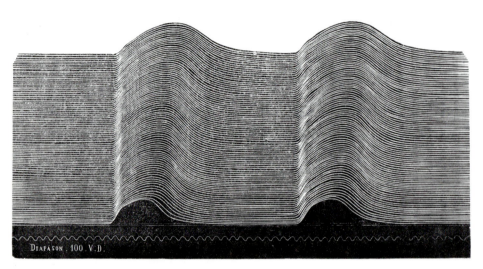

51. Graphic notations of muscular shocks. Taken from Marey,
Du mouvement.

52. Hans Hartung, *A 33*, 1962 (acrylic on canvas, 61 x 46 cm.).

It is essential to make clear that the Mareyan image did not copy reality. Although it captured it entirely and rigorously, reality was transposed. In the case of the first Marey, for example, the artery and heart were converted into graphic curves and a succession of peaks and indentations (see the discussion of dicrotism in Chapter 1), as interpreted by the sphygmo- and cardiograph. The myogram or muscle graph likewise produced a collection of multigrooves or microvibrations (figure 51).

The effect is like looking at a Hans Hartung canvas, the modern master of fine striation and scratching (figure 52). "Hartung," writes one of his commentators, "remembered, in 1953, in [Roger] Lacourière's studio, having scratched the copper plate as if with a comb.... Until then he painted with various kinds of brushes, like all painters.... From then on, he would rake with ever finer combs and scrapers which he had kept from visits to engraving studios."[3] His aim, too, was to represent, in his own way, bursts, jerks and violence, but I shall leave the debatable similarities there. Marey had matched him at portraying kinetics in a universe increasingly given over to speed; painters would indeed soon have to get in training to take up the challenge of this violence. Fernand Léger recognized this: "The thing that is imagined is less fixed.... When one crosses a landscape by automobile or express train, it becomes fragmented; it loses in descriptive value but gains in synthetic value. The view through the door of the railroad car or the automobile windshield, in combination with the speed, has altered the habitual look of things."[4]

The news of an unknown continent – the first results of its tumultuous script – was all that was needed for Marey's science, whether he wanted it or not, to spill over the borders of contemporary knowledge.

To properly delineate what, for convenience, I have called "the third Marey" – the one who gave a decisive impetus to the emerging culture industry – I have to return to two specific questions, because the work, previously outlined, began to move in this direction (art). If, for didactic reasons, I have not yet examined these developments, let me do so now. First, I must turn to "the running horse," to the chronography or biogrammatology of a flashing pattern that had shocked Stanford and inspired Muybridge.

A conflict would soon erupt in Europe over the results of this young, experimental discipline (graphy), and what sight, which it (graphy) dismissed, could pick up. Artists seemed to rely on sight, which could be misleading, and ignore the revelations of recording devices. They were thus accused of being set in their ways, on the wrong track, indeed, unenterprising, mindless, even blind; they had painted what they could not or should not have seen! They had put out misshapen and physiologically inconceivable poses: what condemnation! Could art be so debased by a science of data collection?

The complex story of the clash between Marey and hippographic art must now be examined. I shall only look at three artists: Carle Vernet, Théodore Géricault and J. L. E. Meissonier, with special attention to the latter because he played an overt part in this (methodological) drama. It should be remembered that the question was not a minor one in the nineteenth century. The carriage and running horse belonged to a "genre" in which painters of animals and hunting scenes excelled. The horse, however, was at the same time inseparable from the battle epic. Those who depicted battles could not accomplish their work without representing the horse in its many poses, including at rest – as in Napoleon astride his famous white horse.

The painter Meissonier is a case in point. This hyperrealist, known for his meticulous precision and taste for detail, turned his attention to the events of the Empire (Wagram, Jena, Solferino). He had painted troopers on horseback, their harnesses, dragoons charging

53, 54. Positions of the horse galloping, according to Muybridge and
Meissonier. Taken from Duhousset, *Le Cheval dans la nature et l'art*.

and units of cavalrymen. He distrusted the picturesque. This is why Marey's analyses and Muybridge's parallel discoveries excited him. He initiated contact with them immediately. He participated so extensively in discussions and exchanges about the "different paces of the horse" (especially the existence of its incredible levitation, which had already astonished Stanford, prompting him to consult Muybridge) that when Muybridge came to Paris, he was received by Meissonier with Marey present, as well as the entire art world (November 26, 1881). They talked of "collaborating on a book on the horse, illustrated with Muybridge's photographs and annotated by Meissonier and Marey" (figures 53, 54). In addition, in *Meissonier: His Life and His Art*, we read: "Leland Stanford, Governor of California, asked me to paint his portrait in 1881.... On the table, by the side of the famous cane, lies an open album. It contains the first horses and animals in motion photographed by the American, Muybridge."[5]

Meissonier thus found himself among the protagonists of the question of the day. We also should remind ourselves of what his biographers have told us about this semi-competitor of Marey and Muybridge: In his grounds at Passy, he devoted himself to close examination of the horse in its various movements: "He set up the more original experiment of a little railway...along which he propelled himself on a trolley, his lynx-eye fixed on the parallel course of a horse ridden by a servant a few paces from him."[6]

As befitted his hyperrealist outlook, he first created "models" using plaster and wax, and later easily maneuverable horses made of wire, from which he painted in his studio. He did not want to work solely from memory, he wanted to witness real movements if only of a model. He thus turned to two types of substitute for the animal: life-sized models and smaller scale models. "The public had no idea of the extraordinary care which he readily put into his sculptural maquettes to make them correct...."[7] Neither the pose, the shadow it cast nor the dimensions, nothing was left simply to guesswork.

What were the results? On the one hand, Meissonier had to admit "the faithfulness" of

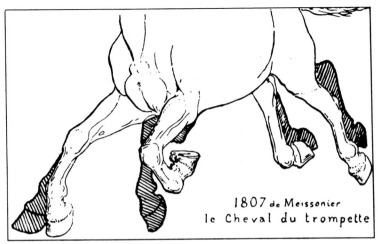

1807 de Meissonier
le Cheval du trompette

55. Sketch of the modifications made by Meissonier to a watercolor copy
of his painting *1807*.

Marey's images, confirmed by Muybridge. On the other hand, he played down their importance and seemed to be critical of them. Meissonier held that "for the artist, there exists only one category of movements, those which his eye can grasp. He no more has the right to put on canvas what is visible with the aid of a sole lens than to paint what a microscope would show him."[8] The photographic snapshot was only valuable to the anatomist or biologist; sensation did not have to abdicate to science. Art was a matter of seeing, not knowing. What a sensible rebellion!

Meissonier would soon narrow the rebellion's scope. Thus, having received the commission for his painting *1807*, the painter made a watercolor of it, which was exhibited in 1889. He modified the horses to take account of information from the laboratory "recorders." He did not extend their front legs as he had earlier, which he now bent. In the adjoining sketch (figure 55), the shaded areas represent the lines of the painting, while the clear ones show the extent of the modification (to the watercolor). This comparative study is due to Emile Duhousset, the hippology expert, who congratulated the painter on it. Meissonier adopted an eclectic solution: he vaunted art's independence, but nevertheless adopted information supplied by science. He objected, then submitted.

But the problem seems more pressing than ever: Did Marey influence the representational arts? Did he indeed point them in the right direction? The answer is not simple. If, in one sense, he freed the arts, in another he somewhat restricted them. In his book *Movement*, he devoted a whole chapter to "Human Locomotion from an Artistic Point of View"; while there was a long discussion of the horse in Chapter 11 "from the points of view of art and science." "Art and science," he wrote, "come together in the search for truth [*exactitude*]. The same methods serve equally well for determining the various attitudes in which an artist should represent a horse...."[9]

However, a few pages earlier, Marey prudently specifies that: "We are not qualified to speak of Aesthetics, still less to discuss the question as to whether Art has the right to represent violent actions, or whether it should restrict itself...."[10] And: "We must not, however, spend time on these reflections, for by criticizing the details of works, which are excellent in other respects, we may expose ourselves to the warning, '*Ne sutor, ultra crepidam.*' "[11]

This reservation had not prevented, nor would it prevent, his making disparaging remarks. The following is typical: The moderns were blatantly accused of having made facile choices, depicting animals resting or in docile poses. Where this had not been possible, they cleverly avoided the problem by using blurred outlines and swirls; horses colliding with each other in a sort of muddle of dust clouds in which the lines were lost. The old masters, less of a target, did not avoid violent and impetuous movement but "the figures sometimes appear in positions of unstable equilibrium."[12] Marey took this opportunity to advise the artist: "Nature herself may fairly be appealed to in deciding.... Instantaneous photography is an excellent means of showing the actual attitudes assumed [by a runner]."[13]

Moreover, when Marey carefully refrained from naming those he found fault with, he would still refer to Duhousset, who had analyzed certain works by modern artists and pointed out their failings (Marey, *La Nature*, September 28, 1878); hence, indictment through intervening attorney.[14] They passed judgment on the horses in St. Mark's Square; the horses of Marly by Guillaume Coustou; ones by Albrecht Dürer (including *The Knight and Death*), ancient bas-reliefs, numerous equestrian statues and the frieze on the Parthenon. They set themselves up as a tribunal to judge art's fidelity.

One of his (or their) victims, Carle Vernet, son of the landscape painter Joseph Vernet, had devoted himself to horses, hunting scenes and races. He was guided by the English morphometrician, George Stubbs, famous for his plates and catalogues of horses, and author of *Anatomy of the Horse* (the English equivalent of Goiffon and Vincent's *Mémoire artificielle*); his work, however, was nonetheless full of "errors" of proportion. He painted animals galloping, but either the back legs bucked just when a hurdle was about to be jumped (a complete contradiction), or "Every animal is trotting and that is all there is to represent pace," as Duhousset put it.[15] In short, he had all the faults: error, the easy solution and the conventional.

However, I now come to the crucial moment. It seems there was a particular aversion to Géricault, the least precise of them all (figure 56), even though he was one of the most hippographic and passionate about the horse, which gave him a living and caused his death.[16] The matter deserves consideration because, although Marey anticipated the future and brought upheaval to the culture of his time, he erred on this question, being too set on the importance of the documentary role of art.

Géricault, the romantic, certainly made mistakes. He wanted to convey the exhilaration and fire of the action, and consequently stretched his horses, elongating them in the direc-

56. Géricault, *The Epsom Derby*, 1821. The Louvre, Paris.

tion of the fight, while at the same time raising their legs almost to a horizontal position. They thus became "hyper-flying horses" which no photographer could capture (*The Epsom Derby*). But hadn't Géricault done more for pictorial dynamics and the representation of energy than the neoclassical painters of the school of David, Meissonier or the supine technicians? Duhousset found him wanting: a clever draughtsman, but, as he readily wrote, "he lacked scientific resources."[17]

What should one choose: the precise or the suggestive? Baudelaire seemed to have gotten around the trap; there were four or five options: (1) *Follow information from the retina.* A solution open to objection, and not much better than the strictly academic approach of reproducing the same clichés with no invention. (2) *The mystagogic or extravagant option.* Apart from the fact that Baudelaire was not for it, this option suppressed the question rather than resolving it. (3) *Adopting the results of recording science and its machines.* A hyper-realism, which was Meissonier's and Marey's, that seemed a partial failure. (4) *Going beyond the cylinder and its sensitive stylus to a metaconcentration.* This could involve every pertinent graphic line to give us a hyperkinetics; an extrapolation having all the tensions, "the essential" (Géricault). Realists and even hyperrealists might balk, but a painter of genius would achieve this broad and powerful synthesis (mnemotechnique, to use Baudelaire's term). False in detail because true as a whole: fury itself. (5) I shall consider presently the fifth possibility, which in a way reconciles 3 and 4; the *Nude Descending a Staircase* (Marcel Duchamp, figure 58); the different phases of motion dissolving into each other.

Géricault had not lied; or rather, as Baudelaire wrote, talking about the landscape painters: "These things are infinitely closer to the truth because they are false, whereas the majority of landscape painters are liars precisely because they have neglected to lie" (the 1859 Salon). Paradoxical and contradictory though it was, the producers of the new graphic images condemned or at least refused to acknowledge someone going in their direction.

Instead of concentrating on one or several moments, Géricault put all of them in at once (intense contraction). The chronophotographic gun remained subservient to the snapshot. It multiplied the shots, of course (twelve to the second), to compensate for its limitations, but Géricault masterfully produced impetus and flight in a single gesture or view. I stress this "misstep": it showed an intransigent positivism — a sort of terrorism — that gladly imposed its way of seeing on the act of seeing itself. And in stressing this mistake, I shall not propose an analysis or laudatory evocation of it.

Let me qualify this reservation: Marey moved still further away from Géricault by introducing, directly or indirectly, a different solution. It was not so much that he blocked the path of art as that he opened up another outlet, that of futurism and kineticism, which is where his modernism lies (figure 57). Nevertheless, it was not necessary to have contested one "response" (the romantic one) in order to favor another (more scientific).

Marey's influence on the painting of his time is indisputable. Drawn to southern Italy, the physiologist had, about 1870, bought a house on the outskirts of Naples, at Posilipo, surrounded by a large area of land used for hunting. Between this villa and the sea rose a tower from where he watched and "aimed at" birds. He was no doubt looked on as a rather eccentric resident: a hunter who was always "shouldering" the gun but never firing. In Naples he was even thought to be a spy and taken to the police station![18]

In southern Italy, where he passed the winter, Marey gave lectures and produced his chronophotographs, which seemed to belong to art as much as science. It was about this time that futurism appeared. Insofar as futurism sought to participate in the modern world that was beginning to emerge, seized by speed and violence (the two being inseparable), it would attempt to represent dynamism. Prefuturists, no doubt, found precisely what they

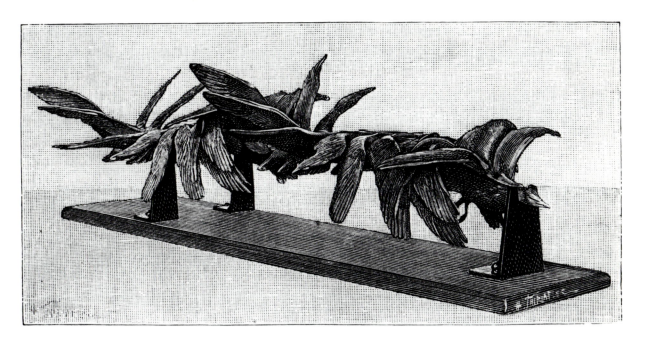

57. Engraving of a bronze sculpture of the flight of the seagull sculpted by
Marey, 1887. Taken from Marey, *Le Vol des oiseaux*.

were looking for in chronophotograms: the language and tools of kineticism; the rejection of still photography and inert representation, with the false realism of its motionless details.

F. T. Marinetti's manifesto did not appear until 1909 (Marey died in 1904), but Giulio Bragaglia was familiar with and inspired by Marey's graphic images. His "trajectories" (chronodynamisms) in turn influenced Giacomo Balla, who drew birds in flight and other chronopaintings. These hastened the arrival of the futurist movement (Luigi Russolo, Umberto Boccioni and others). The filiations and collisions seem undeniable; I have borrowed these details from historians of futurism to show the true position of Mareyism within the revolution in the plastic arts, which it partly provoked. I am not offering an interpretation, but pointing out the fact.[19]

Marey made it possible for the avant-garde to become receptive to new values: instead of escape into the past, the unreal or the dream, there was the double cult of machines and their propulsion (high-speed vehicles, planes, jumps, races). Icarus was replaced by propellers and monoplanes, simple movement by locomotives and even bicycles – it was the "*regno meccanico.*" One could hear the beating and hum of Marey's motors as well as his hearts. This was the double idolatry of powerful machines and their speed – the simultaneous overtaking of space and time!

Futurism wanted to deliver Italy, decaying under the weight of professors, antiquaries and archaeologists. Thus, one can understand how it reserved a special place for monoplanes and tele-inscriptions (the telegraph, the marconigram, the arrival of electricity with its receivers and conductors), in other words, for Marey's devices and science, a science itself guided by a determination to penetrate the finest of tremors (bird locomotion and the movement of hovering insects), as well as the most overpowering (the waves on the Italian coast, swells and flows, wind tunnels, visualizing smoke patterns, hydrodynamics and so on).

He surely can be glimpsed between the lines of the inflammatory statements in Marinetti's manifesto, when it finally appeared: "Up to now literature has exalted a pensive immobility, ecstasy, and sleep. We intend to exalt aggressive action, a feverish insomnia, the racer's stride, the mortal leap, the punch and the slap. We say that the world's magnificence has been enriched by a new beauty: the beauty of speed.... We want to hymn the man at the wheel...."[20] These are undeniable strains of Marey.

In 1902, Boccioni had already proposed "motor-sculptures" and even "electric" and "talking" ones, as a way of leading art out of its fatal hieraticism. There was no end of praise for the quasi-robotic, the train or plane, "whose propeller snaps like a flag." Tumult and impetuosity would have their due expression. One artist close to the Italian futurists, Marcel Duchamp, recognized his debt to Marey. He reaffirms my comments on the practical importance and artistic consequences of Mareyan physiology and biomechanics, which shook up representational art by simultaneously valorizing it (the graphic mark) and assaulting it, demanding its modification (to include energy).

It is known that Duchamp had read Marey, whom he quotes, and that he also knew his work through his brother, Raymond Duchamp-Villon, a medical student working under Marey's assistant and follower, Albert Londe, a radiologist and clinical photographer at Salpêtrière.[21] Duchamp acknowledged that he had been affected by the graphics of decomposition and captured movement. Indeed, about 1910, Duchamp, founding member of "the Puteaux group," decided to champion "so-called scientific cubism" in contrast to the intuitive and subjective kind, which depicted an object or subject from every side and angle at once on a single canvas, using the familiar technique of "fore-shortening" but omitting movement, "the fourth dimension." Duchamp and his group set out to include it; hence, he produced, among other 1912 works, the *Nude Descending a Staircase* (figure 58), a living projectile launched at the viewer. There was a veritable Mareyan explosion of "solidified movements": the drawing, *Two Nudes: One Strong and One Swift* and *The King and Queen Traversed by Swift Nudes*; a watercolor, *The King and Queen Traversed by Nudes at High Speed*; and a painting: *The King and Queen Surrounded by Swift Nudes*! It should be noted that the Salon des Indépendents of February 1912 was to exhibit *Nude Descending a Staircase*, but the organizers opposed it. Duchamp withdrew it. In America, at the Armory Show in New York (February 1913), it provoked a scandal. In any case, one can see broken lines pressing against each other and, in particular, arcs of circles (dots) at the level of the calf and at the joints, which come straight out of Marey's chronophotographs. He, too, as we saw, marked the subject dressed in black with stripes and markers on the areas that moved most. Here, unquestionably, was a child of Marey.

Why then such a scandal? In the first place, the classical nude or posed, academic photograph could be considered a "still life" [*nature morte*]. In this pose, the erotic body, usually recumbent, was distanced, almost mummified; depicting young women climbing or descending a staircase, or going about everyday tasks (such as sweeping) amounted to resuscitating them. This was probably the first provocation.[22]

The second was the identification of these bodies with collections of springs and vibrations, resulting in an "overtly mechanical painting." Not long afterward, Duchamp produced *Rotary Glass Plate* (1920), *Discs Bearing Spirals* (1923) and his various bachelor machines. We might mention here the strange Charles Cros, another specialist in cylinder recording who was devoted to traces and the sound daguerreotype; he was also author of *Principes de mécanique cérébrale* (1879). He writes: "A long, hard campaign in this art of kinetic invention has given me the idea of a project which may be summed up as follows: renouncing direct observation of the structure of the apparatuses of perception, thought and reaction, and constructing a priori devices to perform these functions, taken as the only data."[23] This passionate constructor (the man-machine) transformed the brain and sense organs into kinetic

58. Marcel Duchamp, *Nude Descending a Staircase*, 1912.

instruments, sight into a kind of "rotating disc." At the end of the century, the amazing spectacle of electrical motors that seemed to function before one's very eyes, inspired paintings that tried to suggest dynamism: a pure turbulence. On every side, the simultaneous eclipsed the successive; time seemed to be reintroduced into space and added to its three dimensions. Phantasmagoria and cinematics made a rather amusing couple.

Futurism and kinetic cubism also translated into art what had first been discovered by the new physiology of movement as well as animal machinery. Thus, if, in one sense, Mareyism limited the artist's imaginary world and reminded him of the obligation to respect the real, which he had to transfer onto paper, canvas, metal and so forth – particularly in the running of horses – in another sense, it reaped a whirlwind and helped the plastic artist to express blinding speed and the uninterrupted: he was moving toward the incredible.

I shall now consider the second development, namely the "quarrel" concerning Marey – and it is a particularly heated and involved one. Either he was a crucial innovator and driving force, or his influence was limited. I opt for the first hypothesis. I hold that Marey was at the origins of the airplane and air travel (Chapter 2); that he mobilized figurative painting (futurism and kineticism), and that he directly promoted the culture industry and, in a larger sense, the modernization of perception.

The heart of the problem is to discover whether this is true. I shall briefly recall the general results of chronophotography with a pellicle, a device both light and quick, developed between 1882 and 1890. Marey replaced the old bulky contraption that he had first used – the sensor with a bulb, air transmission and the writing stylus – with increasingly effective optical mechanisms. He was able to abandon his rolling wagon (chronophotography with a fixed glass plate in a camera obscura), and take up a sort of camera that could easily reload in daylight thanks to the bobbin-roll "with a black paper tail" (which he conceived in 1891, and which George Eastman adopted in 1892). He had somehow or other solved a difficult problem, that of the film having to stop intermittently (for the duration of a shot) and then resume its winding from one bobbin to the other.

Marey's system, however, which he had defined from the start and always respected (and which would give us the airplane), required one final operation: analysis was worthless unless it was confirmed by a synthesis. A given phenomenon had to be "reproduced" (by a corresponding image or graphic mark) but it then had to be "produced" (reversibility). Could he dare hope that the ribbon that did the recording could be the means to project what had been recorded onto a screen (reconstitution)?

In a paper delivered to the Academy of Science on May 2, 1892, Marey declared: "It is possible to give the eye the sensation of real movement by projecting (chronophotographic) images in succession onto a screen by means of an instrument which I shall have the honor of presenting to the Academy at an upcoming meeting." This would seem more than enough to conclude that Marey thought up the principle of the automated cinematograph. Given this, why the controversy and endless debate?

On the one hand, even Marey was not interested in perfecting the device, even though it would have cost him nothing. His moving "projector" needed only a proper regulator for its procession of images that would ensure smooth functioning. Without absolutely equal transitions, at equal speed (at least twelve or sixteen per second), the image would not produce the desired dissolve effect. If this relative yet real deficiency is emphasized, then the credit for the invention cannot go to Marey. On the other hand, no one so longed for nor so ably conceived of the principle of the cinematograph.

Marey was not content with the "approximate" or vague half-truths. For proof, I give the last chapter of *Movement* (Auguste Lumière's discovery dates from 1895). It is entitled

59. Sketch of Plateau's hand-held phenakistoscope.

"Synthetic Reconstruction of the Elements of an Analyzed Movement"; and Chapter 7 also deals with the evolution of his method: "Reproduction, Enlargement and Reduction of Chronophotographs."[24] We read in the latter: "The strip of film itself…can produce a series of effects following one another in such rapid sequence that the spectator sees the movement reproduced in all its phases. This synthetical representation of movement will be described further on."[25] Another relevant passage reads: "We have therefore constructed a special apparatus, in which an endless length of film containing forty or sixty figures, or even more, is allowed to pass without cessation under the field of the objective. [The illumination] projects these figures upon a screen. This instrument produces very bright images.…"[26]

However, Marey was not that concerned with the final adjustments, which Louis Lumière would soon take up (1895). Thus is he passed over and his importance diminished. Yet, he had glimpsed the answer so precisely and with such dedication that he has also, quite rightly, been seen "as the inventor of cinematography," to quote the expert opinion of Lucien Bull, another who is determined to give Marey his due.[27] Depending on what aspects are stressed, this debate could go on indefinitely. But while the final "trick" was due to Lumière's ingenuity, the spirit of a cultural machine that could bring the image to life came from Marey, who called for and designed it.

To give his case more substance, I would like to pursue three points:

1. It was known, beginning with Joseph Plateau's phenakistoscope (figure 59), that the luminous image lasted only a moment. The following image thus had to come into sight while the previous one had still not entirely disappeared for this to be seen as continuous movement. The eye transforms succession into a rapid dissolve. If "the views" were projected fast enough, this could easily create the illusion of uninterrupted and transitory movement. The same apparatus that had broken up movement would restore it just as quickly and well, as long as it was turned at the same speed.

It is striking how many projection and reproduction machines suddenly appeared in the mid-nineteenth century. Along with Plateau's phenakistoscope, there was William G. Horner's zootrope, Emile Raynaud's praxinoscope, Henri Joly's photozootrope, Raoul Grimoin-Sanson's phototachygraph, Coleman Sellers's kinematoscope, H. Cook's photobioscope, Henry Heyl's phasmastrope and Thomas Edison's famous kinetoscope, as well as Léon Bouly's "cinematograph," the name he gave his device in 1893 and which would eventually prevail.

This is not an exhaustive list; but all lacked the final mechanism that allowed the film to be wound in a regular way, with equidistant and intermittent stops, or equal spacings for fixed, synchronous projection by the shutter. For if the image continued to move, even very slightly, the tiniest gesture would inevitably be blurred. As with the case of getting the image in (the shot), unwinding/winding had to be coupled with equal fixity.

Louis Lumière generally solved the problem by perforating the edges of the film, a method probably taken from Edison and refused by Marey. Two small teeth fitted into the holes in the strip, pulling it down – the measured length of one image – then, having let go, went back up empty so as to be able to grip the next one to move it down.

2. Marey gave his assistant Georges Demenÿ the task of finding out how to do this. How should one understand this delegation, which verged on abandonment? In his book *Movement*, Marey acknowledged the passing on of the work: "Having arrived at this point in our researches, we learned that our mechanic had discovered an immediate solution of this problem, and by quite a different method; we shall therefore desist from our present account pending further investigations."[28] Why, under the circumstances, did Marey turn away from the final adjustments?

The fact is that he preferred analysis to synthesis; the latter rendered visible what had first been made invisible. "What they [moving photographs] show, the eye could have seen directly," wrote Marey, "they have added nothing to the power of our sight, reduced none of its illusions. The true character of a scientific method is to supplement the shortcomings of our senses and correct them."[29] It was surely this hidden aversion to phantasmagoria, a refusal of false appearances, and, conversely, an attraction to what distances us from the sensory, that provided the framework for this apparent renunciation.

The positivist reflex was once more at play; a rather rigid scientism distanced Marey from inventing. It was not a matter of chance that theoretical success was accompanied by lack of interest and partial failure in the practical sphere. Marey preferred absorbing the spectacle of the world into graphs rather than the opposite. He had no interest in the artifice of fictitious moving images.

Demenÿ, in fact, almost solved the problem of reversible chronophotography (he took out a patent on October 10, 1893). Briefly, two cylinders (c_1 and c_2) turned at the same speed, one feeding the other (figure 60). The regular "stops" were maintained by a cam, an oval bobbin located between the aperture and the cylinder c_2. The film was taken around this, making its progress uneven (Charles Gaumont collaborated with Demenÿ on this) "with the result that, because of the actual form of the winding surface, the movement transmitted to the film roll would be regular, with stops measured as required" (hence the request for a patent in 1893). The solution could not be entirely satisfactory, if only because the exaggeration produced by the intermediary bobbin meant that the final images were less distanced from each other and so less sharp. The goal, however, was being approached (in 1893), as is indicated by Marey's words in *Movement*: "We learned that our mechanic had discovered an immediate solution of this problem."

Marey and Demenÿ had an argument at this point, and it should not be overlooked. Demenÿ resigned from the station in 1894. Marey could not agree to his assistant marketing his invention (Gaumont), especially because he intended to use photographs on paper,

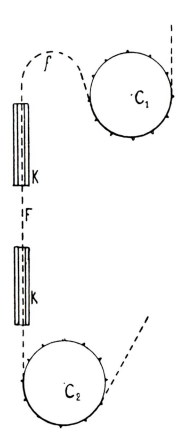

60. Diagram of the winding of film by a cam. Process patented by Demenÿ
    in 1893. Taken from Bull, *La Cinématographie*.

realized with the help of the chronophotographic instruments and processes of the station, Marey's own, even though Marey had not even been consulted (he was in Naples).[30] Here is additional evidence that the master scarcely helped his pupil along the road to practical application for his devices (reversibility).

My conclusion stands: Marey, so close to the goal, preferred a scientific path over integration in a quasi-industrial one. The latter certainly verified the quality and fidelity of what had been taken from reality in that it reconstituted it, but his only interest in such success was its experimental repercussions.

3. A third remark: Demenÿ would, in a different way, extend and complete Mareyism. It seems fairly clear that, from the outset (*Du Mouvement dans les fonctions de la vie*, phon-autography, 1868), Marey set out to translate the world of vibrations, from whatever source, into graphic curves and tracings. I pointed out (in Chapter 1) the mobilizing role of annexing sound to the visual, from "the acoustics of the eyes" dear to Jules Lissajous to Hermann von Helmholtz's "synthesis of vowels." Marey took up, in his own way, where the work of phoneticians and steno- and pianographers had left off.

"At the beginning of the year 1875," wrote Charles Rosapelly who worked in Marey's laboratory (*Travaux du Laboratoire*, 1876), "a delegation from the Society of Linguistics, led by its president, [Léon] Vaïsse, came to see Professor Marey in order to find out if the graphic method could be applied to the study of the varied and complex movements that occurred in speech; if it could provide an objective trace of the acts performed...."[31] Marey had already given his reply; he thus honored this request for a material expression "of the essentially fleeting phenomena which the ear can neither analyze nor compare with any certainty," as he put it in *La Méthode graphique*.[32] He listed all the advantages of such an analysis, pointing out the benefits to be gained from it by deaf-mutes.

Marey was aware that Edison, working alongside Muybridge, had in 1877 applied for a patent for a machine for the transmission of sounds. In France, on April 16, 1877, Cros addressed a letter to the Academy of Science on the subject of a "process of recording and reproducing phenomena perceived by the ear" ("seeing noise").

The trace of a song's cadences was transformed into indents and microreliefs, preferably on a thin metal plate, which was now replacing the lamp-blacked cylinder. This, in return, reproduced the voice through the vibration of a diaphragm. *La Nature* discussed the exploits of the talking machine, but chronophotography preferred to explore the invisible and its transduction. It seemed undeterred by the most subtle movements: those of the facial muscles; it captured the slightest sigh, the vibrations of the vocal chords (the laryngoscope) and the movement of the lips. Here was precisely the novel assemblage conceived of by Demenÿ: the photophone, a new synthesizer. It was a classic phenakistoscope – but was equipped with an electric motor for the use of deaf-mutes – in that it made visible the slightest stirrings of the mouth, and reassembled and made life-size the physiognomy of the face. The subject, for example, would shout, "*Vive la France!*" (figure 61); Demenÿ had the sixteen images replace each other in one second so as not to lose what he termed "the suppleness" of the moving images: no jumps or vibrations in the show!

The double synthesis or linking together of "image and sound" was produced by a special zootropic device at the end of 1891. It was patented in 1892, and tried and tested in front of the pupils of the school for deaf-mutes in Paris, in the presence of H. Marichelle, a teacher at the institute. Marey had recently published a study of chronophotography in the *Revue Générale des Sciences* in 1891, and the young teacher of deaf-mutes at the institute realized how useful this alternative method of phonography might be. He contacted the learned physiologist, who entrusted the matter once again to his assistant Demenÿ.[33]

This phonoscope prompted Demenÿ to reflect on the amazing potential of "talking photographs":

61. Chronophotographic analysis of speech movements. Portrait of Demenÿ pronouncing the phrase "Vive la France." Taken from *La Nature* (April 1892).

How many people would be happy if they could for a moment see again the living features of someone who had passed away! The future will replace the still photograph, locked in its frame, with the moving portrait, which can be given life at the turn of a wheel! The expression of the physiognomy will be preserved as the voice is by the phonograph. The latter could even be added to the phonoscope to complete the illusion.... We shall do more than analyze [the face]; we shall bring it to life again.[34]

Basically, what Demenÿ had proposed, at Marey's request, was a new acoustics of the eyes, a "photography of speech," just as he could translate a show into a melody for the blind (to hear colors as one sees words). This was surpassing both Edison and Cros.

If I seem to be spending time on details and consequences, it is to foreground the archaeology of the audiovisual, the successful search for the full reconstitution of scenes (total synthesis). I can hardly fail to see here the foundations of the talking cinema. Louis Lumière thus completed, in 1895, something that was already underway.

I do not doubt that, when all is said and done, Marey and his laboratory's work played a decisive part in what was about to unexpectedly take flight: the rush of "talking pictures," the cinematograph.

The title of Lumière's first patent, taken out on February 13, 1895 — suffices in itself to confirm a direct pedigree. Marey had heralded and theorized "the machine" but was beaten to the post; there was a kind of poetic justice in this.[35] For, when it came down to it, the new application smacked too much of illusionistic games, and indeed supported them. Marey had always turned away from a "seeing" that misled, while the cinematograph plunged us in just that. He preferred other ventures, such as the one he entrusted to Demenÿ, namely transposing from one register to another to make "hearing" visible. Although it has been contested, Marey took part in what now characterizes our world.

The smallest spark rekindled debate about his merits. On March 25, 1924, at the Academy of Medicine, for example, Charles Richet chose to revive it. He saw the Lumière brothers as clever constructors (their toothed device for winding film), but proposed to demonstrate that "Marey is the sole inventor of the cinematograph."[36] Indeed, there were many problems and disputes to be settled before a plaque could be put up, in 1924, on the building of the Grand Café, on the boulevard des Capucines, to commemorate the first cinematographic performances.

The Commission for Old Paris was obliged to embark on a thorough investigation, especially since the members of the Academies of Science and Medicine demanded that Marey's name be included along with the Lumière brothers. The French Society of Photography also entered the debate. It was finally settled by a compromise: there would be two ceremonies and two plaques, one for the Lumière brothers and the other on the house where Marey had lived, not far from the Physiological Station, at 11 boulevard Delessert. It would say that Marey had taken part in the invention of cinematography. Indeed, in my view, he deserved to be associated with this historic commemoration.[37]

———

I strongly maintain the thesis that Mareyism contained within it, perhaps unwittingly, the foundations of the modern world it foreshadowed: the signals and fluxes, the multiple tele-inscriptions, the long-range controls and sensitive recorders and, more obviously, travel in the air (airplanes) and underwater; the capacity to preserve traces; abstract art and the crucial domain of audiovisual communication.

Marey was not, of course, passionately involved in all the applications and entrusted work to his assistants Tatin, Demenÿ, Rosapelly, François-Franck and others.

On several counts, however, a faithful disciple of Auguste Comte, he reminds us that a

62. View of the track at the Physiology Station taken from inside the laboratory. Taken from Marey, *Movement*.

science shines through what it makes possible. Its beneficial effects enshrine and validate it. This is why analyses of human walking led to a better use of muscular force: "to traverse the greatest distance with the least expenditure of energy" (for soldiers); or again: "to cover a certain distance in the shortest possible time."[38] These would go on to include the horse pulling loads or carriages.[39] Marey was, in fact, asked by the Minister of War to do a study and then present a detailed report.[40] In the factory, too, an optimization of gesture would be achieved thanks to the new graphic physiology: "The same method would lend itself to the teaching of movements necessary in various vocations. It would show how the stroke of a skilled blacksmith differed from that of an apprentice. It would be the same for all manual acts...."[41] Through this (a cinematics), Marey seemed to have founded ergonomics.

As he pointed out, gymnasts and other athletes – such as fencers, throwers, jumpers and runners – would also benefit and be able to perform more effectively. To this end, Marey perfected a fixed hodograph (figure 62), as well as many other measuring devices (dynamometers, chronographs...). The fixed hodograph seemed to unite the old and the modern, both mechanical and electrical "capture." The old lamp-blacked cylinder indeed reappeared, but each time the walker passed one of the telegraph poles placed along the station's track – at 50 m intervals – he would break the the line's circuit: "Inside the laboratory, a recording apparatus – the fixed odograph – is in communication with the telegraph line."[42] The end result was a zigzag curve, which, though lacking in detail, gave a preliminary indication of pace; the ground covered and time taken being known, their relation would express speed. Marey continued in this direction, no longer in order to measure speed but to establish the sequence of phases in a complex act; the pole vault, long jump, falling, wrestling and boxing. The famous chronograms that had a geometrical quality split up and revealed the positions of the limbs; their swinging, bending, spacing and so on (figures 63, 64). They gave an instant indication of where improvements might be made,

63, 64. Gymnastic movements at the parallel bars, around 1883.

because "in jumping from a height, the difference between landing gently with no shock and landing with rigid legs is clearly seen. . . ."[43] From now on, exercise could be done judiciously, achieving results at less expense and in a harmonious manner. The eye could not grasp – the Mareyan leitmotif – what only an instrument could record and restore.

Once again, Demenÿ would have the task of entering this revolutionary field of experiment. In my view, Marey and Demenÿ would throw their epoch into turmoil. What other scientist did as much to shake it up? Demenÿ was asked to take the work forward and explore this new continent because, in 1880, he had begun a school, the Circle for Rational Gymnastics. "We needed assistance," he wrote, "so Paul Bert introduced us to Professor Marey, who was well known for his explanations of the methods of the exact sciences in biology. . . . After an exchange of views and ideas, we established a study program to serve as an introduction to requests for grants sent to the city of Paris and to the State."[44] The city council granted money and land in 1881, and increased the budget in 1882. In his account of their collaboration, Demenÿ added: "I was entrusted by M. Marey, who was away from Paris, with organizing and supervising the initial work of setting up the Laboratory which came to be called the Physiological Station. . . . The work begun in 1882 was completed in 1883, and when M. Marey returned from Naples, he was able to take possession of his laboratory, which was ready for work." Naturally, Demenÿ was appointed to the post of assistant at the station (figures 65a, 65b).

Why this attraction to gymnastics and athletic movement? Why the orientation of neuromotor physiology toward human activity? Demenÿ suggests an answer: "If there was [still] no real method, one great thought dominated gymnastic societies [which began to flourish after 1875], namely love of country and the obligation to be strong enough to defend it."[45] Quite unexpectedly, Mareyism would come to the aid of the sons of those humiliated by defeat in 1870. Marey was even asked to help with retraining and preparing soldiers, as well

65a. First site of laboratory before the construction of the Physiological
     Station (1881).

65b. General view of the buildings and installations at the Physiological
     Station in the Parc des Princes in 1889. Taken from Demenÿ,
     "L'Evolution de l'éducation physique."

as designing an educational system. He thus joined several committees of experts, as did Demenÿ, who quickly became known through his early books with their overtly Mareyan titles: *Les Bases scientifiques de l'éducation physique* (1902) and *Mécanisme et éducation des mouvements* (1904).

Industrial economy would later annex Mareyism as an aid in production and productivity. The physiology of locomotion and gesture inspired the new technology of a capitalism based on the organization of the workplace. The scientific analysis of motion and performance led both to the transformation of military training and the ultramechanization of human work.[46] Did Marey thus play a part in the tyranny of assembly lines and Taylorist exploitation? It could be that he was also pushing toward robotization. It was less a man-machine or even a human machine that Marey wanted than a machine capable of replacing man; who was considered a machine of low productivity. It was enough to record and calculate the results of this machine to replace it with something better.

One of his distant followers, Frank Gilbreth, accentuated what had been outlined in Marey's studies in his book *Motion Study* (1912). Its subjects were chronometry and cyclography (a camera on one side and an electric bulb attached to the arms or hands of those performing a specific task: the surgeon, the baseball thrower, the mason). The movements left traces on the sensitized plate; one could then see causes of awkwardness and the uselessness of hesitations. The aim was to instill automatic gestures, dexterity and rapid execution (the recording of movement or cyclography).

Marey and Demenÿ were specifically contacted, and Marey presided over a commission entrusted with revising programs for teaching gymnastics (1887), which submitted its report in 1889. As for Demenÿ, he was appointed in 1890 by the Minister for Public Instruction to study the gymnastic methods practiced in Sweden and Denmark. The Minister of War who had previously enlisted Marey's aid wrote to Demenÿ on August 10, 1901: "The teaching of gymnastics as currently practiced in the army does not seem to respond fully to the desired goal, which is to produce vigorous, robust and athletic soldiers able to endure the exhaustion of war and overcome the obstacles that one encounters in the field. Training based on scientific facts, deduced from an understanding of the physiology of exercise of the body, is alone capable of producing the required results."[47] Demenÿ was asked to join the specialists designing the new army and its training.

Demenÿ, in the spirit of Marey, was opposed to inventing acrobatic stunts, and also to what was called "the Swedish method" (or the Ling method). Without going into detail, the latter seems at once static, restrained and abrupt.[48] Demenÿ, in contrast, like Marey, laid importance – chronophotography required it! – on the body in motion, harmonious and curved. In short, Marey and Demenÿ established the double principle of economy and amplitude. Their aim was less fatigue, the best results and greatest dynamism; the goal was not so much muscular development as exaltation of the motor faculty.

The overall methodological framework that ran throughout all of Marey's work was never neglected; a jump, for example, was first decomposed into parts, the better to synthesize it. Gymnastics reproduced a living cinematograph, performing and recombining swiftly and effortlessly, what had earlier been broken into parts. The athlete ultimately moved forward like film: the same synthesis of phases and moments, the same live projection, the same show![49]

I cannot discuss all of Mareyism's repercussions lest we go on forever. All of the developments we have followed certainly demonstrate his influence. Locomotor analysis liberated the body from an ill-conceived training program that was neither rigorous nor scientific – a case in point being the Swedish method, though it claimed to be both. Analysis spared costly fatigue, restoring to soldiers and pupils alike psychomotor and psychokinetic power. It gave instruction on regular, rhythmic movement (jumping, handling weapons, fighting,

66. Decoration of a panathenaic vase. Taken from Marey, *Movement*.

climbing). The factory was also affected and had to "produce" more at less cost. The life of the body would be greatly enhanced by all this and Demenÿ in fact raised a number of aesthetic questions concerning the influence of exercise on the shape of a body, which was to be constantly straightened, compressed and stretched out: "Chemistry has replaced alchemy, and medicine bone-setting; scientific physical education must replace the frantic inconsistencies of acrobatics and athleticism."[50]

In an utterly Mareyan style, Demenÿ took to examining the many different attitudes of the body ("it is not his clothes he should be ashamed of, it is his appearance"), as well as antique statues (figure 66) such as Myron's *Discobolus* (c. 450 B.C.) and Polykleitos's *Doryphoros* (spear-bearer, c. 450 B.C.). In earlier days, we closely examined hippographics (the horse running). The reason for this interest seems obvious: a new understanding of the body and its potential (psychomotor power) was emerging. I have considered in turn – apart from air travel – the call to modern art to step out of its inertia (futurism and Duchamp); talking cinematography; and, lastly, freedom of movement and élan (jumping and running).

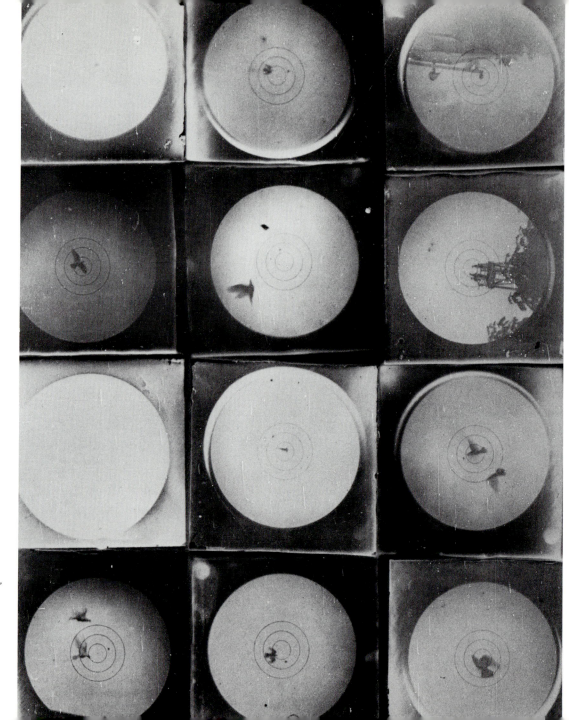

67. Pictures of a bird in flight obtained using the
first photographic gun. Taken from Marey,
"Station physiologique, méthodes et appareils,"
1882–1886.

Conclusion

The science of movement has itself undergone continual and profound movement, and has shifted its center of gravity. Chronophotography must therefore be subjected to a chronophotography of its own, which will reveal three successive moments that are closely linked:

1. It begins by internal movements, even the tiniest ones – the pulse, the muffled beatings of the heart, then respiratory puffs and the slightest organic dilations and stretchings. Marey adopted a rigorous method based entirely on sensitive instruments in the effort to proceed without violence. He is the methodologist and inventor of the lightest and most reliable "sensors" – the sphygmogram, which was the first, the cardiogram, pneumogram, pantogram, thermogram and so on. The list is endless. True physiology could thus measure volume, weight, duration, movement, lines and exertion.

2. It then turns, inevitably, toward the neuromuscular, hence external movements, which were not easier to record (despite being external). These were, in fact, the most ephemeral and ungraspable movements, since Marey examined only the extremes: the rapid, the oscillating, the running horse and birds in flight followed the quivering of insect wings and minuscule vibrating cilia. He was obliged to revise his recording methods (myographs, hodographs, dynamagraphs, simultaneous polygraphs and so on) until he arrived at "optical-electrical capture," which gradually replaced the "mechanical" kind.

The essence of Mareyism is found here, in the inexorable evolution toward subtle instruments, including the famous chronophotographic gun, partly inspired by Jules Janssen's astronomical revolver – which could "pluck out" (or sample) the most distant or minute phenomena without in any way altering them (figure 67). Telecapture! Of course, theoreticians with a psychoanalytic bent could have a field day with this: a gun, capture. What veiled aggression! What voyeurism! The terminology used here seems to have deluded them.

3. Lastly, at the same time, the physiologist gradually moved, despite himself, toward the study of movements elaborated and constructed by man for man's benefit: first, kinetic art (representing speed); cinematography (acting it out); then gymnastics (performing it). Here, again, the psychologist might see an extension of the previous neurosis: in the naked bodies or the woman descending the staircase. These three distinct fields may seem to make up the bulk of the analysis. But this is not so.

The "moving image of and for man" is fundamentally the same; or, in these three dissimilar cases, the same show, the same synthesis. I do not separate Mareyan physical education from the projection of phantasmagorical images or from figurative painting, because, in each of the three situations, there is an attempt to "remake" what had previously been fragmented.

Mareyism is striking because of its filmic unity, although some commentators overemphasize the contrary, namely the extent and variety of its purposes and applications. The idea that it attempted too many things in too many different directions should be rejected.

To give as complete an account as possible, I cannot hide the fact that there is one "movement," the oddest and perhaps most complex of all, that does not fit into the three-part framework. It has to be defined as "external," but at the same time as "internal," caused by man, who alone maintains and passes it on, but from which he also "suffers." In a word, there is an intermediate case that blurs the three aspects I have sought to distinguish.

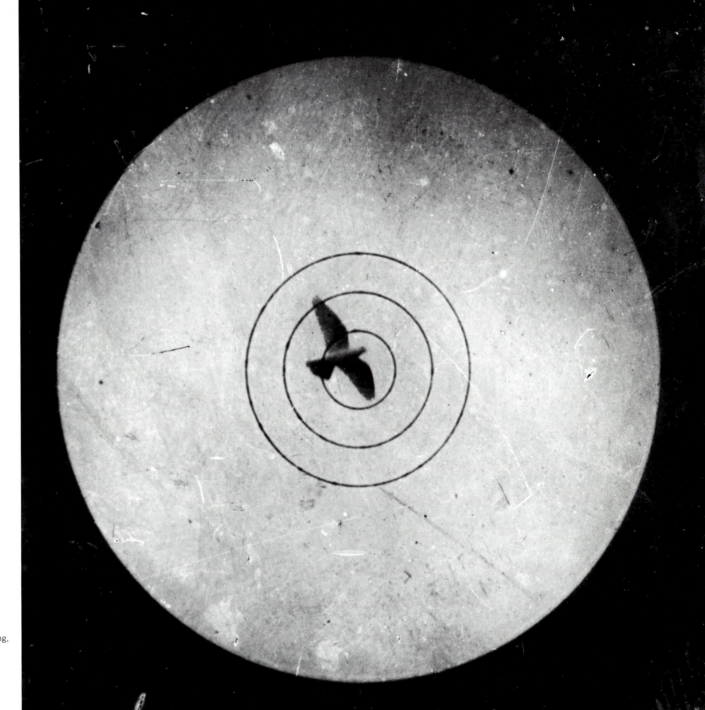

68. Picture of a bird in flight
taken by photographic shooting,
around 1885.

Naturally, Marey devoted several papers to it, presented at the Academy of Medicine, the Academy of Science, and numerous meetings of experts.

I am referring to the scourge of the time, the dreadful Asiatic cholera, and epidemiology as a whole. Though marginal to his own work, Marey made a significant contribution in this area, putting him on a level with Pasteur.

Cholera had occupied him on several occasions in the past because it was characterized by a paradoxical and violent fluctuation in temperature, well demonstrated by the thermograph. This prompted an "Essay on the Physiological Theory of Cholera" in the *Gazette Hebdomadaire de Médecine et de Chirurgie* (1865). In this, Marey examined the two phases: peripheral coldness while the heat at the center increases; and, in a second, reversed phase, a rise in the peripheral temperature, while the internal temperature drops significantly.

In *La Méthode graphique*, Marey took up and extended these observations, focusing on the variable nature of the phenomenon, which made two simultaneous readings in physically far apart places necessary.

In 1884, with a change of perspective, Marey once again entered the fray, using his own method (albeit in a different way) to elucidate the mysterious illness and its transmission, that is, a network of movement as imperceptible as it is subterranean. The reorientation lay in studying cholera from the outside, at a distance, rather than from inside. The preference at the time for external movement could perhaps explain the change (epidemiology).

It was an opportunity, in passing, for Marey to jeer sarcastically at the philosophy and methodology of certain doctors who remained unconvinced of his views. Either they held, for the most part, that the malady was born within the person (following the dictum "the real cholera precedes the official one") and urged rather fanciful treatments to restore health; or that, if the sickness were passed on, the virus responsible could not survive outside the human who sheltered it (the concept of contagion).

Marey presented a solution that was not only different but radically opposed: the infectionist. Water was the vector of the disease. The direction houses faced, the direction of the wind, fog, tight quarters (barracks, schools, prisons, asylums) were irrelevant: "Forgive me for passing over these multiple questions with such velocity and for apparently treating them lightly, since these doctrines have had the privilege of impassioning many members of this Assembly, but I am eager to be done with these hypotheses...."[1]

As Marey pointed out, epidemiologists had already noticed strange patterns in London (the Broad Street pump elicited a long commentary from Marey), as well as in Nîmes, Paris and other places. In the capital, the contagion followed the routes of water distribution. The neighborhoods supplied by water from Grenelle (the wells of which were famous) had been spared, while others, which were dependent on the Ourcq or the Seine, had been affected. Moreover, the top of rue Mouffetard, to number 42, had been sheltered from infection, while below the population had been decimated. The only reason was the fact that artesian water was used as far as number 42.

The reason for the growing catastrophe could be read between the lines of data collected and sifted through from as early as 1832: laundry workers, for example, took a heavier toll than other trades. They handled water from the rivers and washing tanks. The conclusion was self-evident.

Thus, with great audacity and vehemence, Marey called for an "administrative medicine," which would work solely with documents (at a distance), using files, lists and maps. He felt this would bring new and decisive results.

According to Marey, the lethal water had been soiled by the "evacuations" of the sick (suffering from diarrhea), which ended up infecting the wells and contaminating the drains and water courses. "It was almost a novelty," Marey noted, "when, in 1873, Dr. Blanc, at the Congress of the French Association for the Advancement of Science, presented current ideas from England on the transmission of cholera by drinking water. . . . But since the role of water soiled by choleric evacuation is still not considered in this country a predominant cause of the spread of epidemics, I have undertaken to find out, in certain areas affected by cholera, what part this element might play."[2]

Marey immediately set to work and delivered the results of a detailed investigation. He superimposed the topography of the Paris water distribution system, with its canals and its various branches, on a map of the epidemic's progress. The maps coincided. Marey complained about the approximate nature of the tracings and information he had been given, so he chose to carry out his research in the Côte-d'Or, in Beaune and the villages he knew (Meursault, Combertaux, Labergement-les-Seurre), which were crossed by two small rivers, the Tille and the Bèze.

> The reports received by the Academy containing no further topographical indications which would be of use in continuing my research, I resolved to supplement it by seeing how mortality was distributed in an area whose topography I am familiar with, and I had the good fortune to find fairly complete statistical information about my home town. . . . This town (Beaune) is a remarkable example of the spread of cholera by the water of a little river that crosses it. . . .[3]

It was a difficult investigation. It was necessary to follow trails, to know the wells, garbage, drains, high water marks, the streams that ran in the streets and so on.

In a given hamlet, when the river would swell and run over into the streets, the water would rise to the dung heaps. The peasants were in the bad habit of "relieving themselves anywhere," especially on their dung heaps.[4] This observation closed the circle of infection.

In other places, heavy rain carried along all the matter that would contaminate springs and even shallow wells:

In regard to the only part of France where I have been able to supplement the absence of topo-graphical information by my recollections, I find that the course of a small river whose waters have been soiled by the riverside residents and used by them for domestic purposes has spread the illness with an intensity and gravity that are extreme. I also recall that in the vicinity of Beaune, Meursault had been strongly affected by the epidemic of 1849, and I knew that this village was located on a water course which crosses several other localities higher up. I therefore went to Meursault.... The secretary of the town hall had the list of the 103 deaths which occurred in the epidemic of 1849.... A copy of the town registry provided me with the topography of the village and the posi-tion of the water course.[5]

Marey examined the details, and understood and explained the anomalies. He thus invented the science of trails, epidemiological fieldwork, hygiene and preventive medi-cine, the struggle against the conditions of contagiousness. There was little or no point in looking for the true cause (a bacillus discovered by Koch in 1883), because he already knew what steps had to be taken to stop the explosion. He drew up a catalogue of the numerous measures to be enforced, and sent it to the Commission for Hygiene.

This careful study seems a tremendous confirmation of Marey's spirit: cartography; the exploration of a complicated, sinuous movement, often interrupted and resumed; the distancing of the body though illness affected it. There was a need in some sense to stay on the surface and not worry about what was happening inside: a pathospatiography!

————————

Why and how were the results so spectacular? There are three methodological reasons:

1. Marey only really embraced one method, namely unearthing and recording what could not been seen; never was science, initially, so restricted and penetrating. In addition,

he insisted on reproducing tools that had already been used; he made small modifications to them, which extended their use. Inventing nothing, he improved on Karl von Vierordt, Muybridge and Janssen respectively. He set out to lighten devices of their's that were too heavy or had too many elements. He simplified.

"Whosoever kisses too much, hugs badly." Marey not only respected this proverb but illustrated it as well. He limited his attention to an apparently minute problem: the rest would follow like water over falls. A single idea, pushed to its limits, produced the revelations and successes that I have outlined. We remain overwhelmed by the gap between the rather anodyne point of departure – a biological measurement, the pulse's tremor – and the abundance of the final harvest; for, it revolutionized its time and heralded the next century.

2. Another reason for such triumph is that biologists, more than others, fell into the trap of regarding life as ungraspable and multiple. They valorized this and gradually slipped into a stubborn "vitalism," which Marey the positivist berated. When they mechanized, they too often resorted to outdated and rudimentary models. Mareyism, in common with other ingenious mechanists, including Louis Bréguet, Marcel Deprez and Jules Lissajous, and acoustic experts and physiologists of the German school (Karl Ludwig, Emil du Bois-Reymond, Helmholtz), had recourse to increasingly sophisticated means of capturing and transmitting information, first air, then electrical and optical means. Marey modified and aligned his instruments according to what he intended to measure, not the reverse. I repeat my thesis: the Mareyan revolution is characterized by increasingly sensitive and precise "sensors." Physics and chemistry also came to his aid, although we must not forget that he was always on the lookout for help from any direction.

Without these, he would not have had the same success. From its beginnings in the nineteenth century, photography – heliography – sought to perfect its receivers (emulsions), which could be imprinted so as to capture the slightest detail (faithfulness and, ideally, speed of shot). Judaean bitumen was replaced by William Henry Fox Talbot's calotype, which was, in turn, replaced by collodion and finally, around 1890, by gelatine bromide. In the beginning, one had to remain motionless for nearly an hour, in full light to obtain a "take." If the subject moved even a little, the picture would blur and the outlines would be lost. As a result, chairs with fastening devices to hold the back of the neck still were used; or the subject supported him- or herself firmly on a half column to endure the time taken for the shot.

The length of time of the shot and the heaviness of the cameras prevented the new physiology from tracing movements such as the horse's gallop, not to mention a fortiori the wing beats of a dragon fly. In order for his plate to seize movements that would otherwise blur it, Marey employed the new potential of the "snapshot," improved through advances in the chemistry of photographic materials, which were modified (extreme impressionability) in less than a second (the chronophotographic gun). Without these substances, Mareyism would have faced an insurmountable barrier. He needed these products – the framework for new possibilities – that changed at the speed of lightening and retained the trace of the sudden flash.

3. Another reason for his success was that the physiologist chose the most promising path, that of the "moving image" and representation. In other words, he began to listen to the language of nature. He externalized and revealed or, rather, wrote (the scribe) what was hidden or what eluded us due to its smallness.

In trying to see the invisible and imperceptible, he appealed not to sight, which veiled and distorted rather than revealed, but to recording instruments, which were flexible (electrometers, dynamometers, ergometers) and sensitive to variation, flux, current and change.

The resulting graphic expression simplified it and made comparison possible; it alone enabled results to be processed and the discovery of variables. The method also allowed space to be mastered (it miniaturized and condensed data because it only retained the essential) as well as time, which it captured and whose various phases (or positions) it located. The union of the two (space and time) constituted "movement" itself, and hence the chronophotography that measured it.

Above all, once nature had been transposed, relieved of what encumbered and veiled it, it could be recomposed. Marey had always worked at this reciprocal action (the heart or the artificial pump, arteries made of rubber, the mechanical bird and then the airplane, and audiovisual devices which brought to life voices and scenes...). Reconstitutive physiology sought analogy to "the chemistry of synthesis." It seems that, if we leave the solid ground of the real, we lose our way; but if we stay attached to it we lose ourselves. The "image" saves us from these two perils; we can thus consider a helpful "substitute."

Positivism was less successful insofar as it tackled the world itself and its phenomena. What Marey constructed was a "second sort" of positivism. He photographed and transcribed the pulsating and changing dramas of the universe. Before the analysis becomes a panegyric, however, I would recall that this philosophy – a neo- and metamechanical positivism of life – inescapably influenced Marey's opinions. I have pointed out three in this account:

He focused exclusively on the strictly documentary, to the extent of censuring several painters, especially the most daring, those like Géricault. Not only did he find fault with the results of his depictions of running, he didn't even suspect that the artist was producing a synthesis superior to that of his own reductive devices. This was a double mistake: he thought that the painter was arbitrarily transgressing the laws of the real at the precise moment that he was respecting them more than the lens (ultracondensation and hence exaggeration of pathos).

He was not interested in the cinematography that his work had called for, demanded, because it no doubt seemed too "optical" and too illusionistic. The Lumière brothers would steal his thunder, producing a projector with well-regulated reversibility. Demenÿ had brushed with success and had intended to turn his patent to industrial use, but Marey disowned and rejected him.

Lastly, he took part, at least indirectly, in the exploits, but also the exploitation, of human labor based on the Taylorist model. If he caught a glimpse of the importance of the corporeal, its rhythms and psychomotor powers, through dismantling gesture, he hastened standardization, surveillance, production goals and alienation.

These three reservations could be reduced to a single criticism: "over-mechanization." This account of the methods and philosophy of Mareyism has been unabashedly enthusiastic, but this does not stop me from recognizing the other side of the coin.

Notes

EARLY PRINCIPLES

1. Etienne-Jules Marey, *Physiologie médicale de la circulation du sang, basée sur l'étude graphique des mouvements du coeur et du pouls artériel, avec application aux maladies de l'appareil circulatoire* (Paris: Adrien Delahaye, 1863), p. 6.

2. Marey, *Animal Mechanism: A Treatise on Terrestrial and Aerial Locomotion*, International Scientific Series 11 (London: Henry S. King, 1973), p. 1.

3. Ibid.

4. Marey, *La Méthode graphique dans les sciences expérimentales et particulièrement en physiologie et en médecine* (Paris: Masson, 1878), p. 11.

5. Marey, *Physiologie médicale de la circulation du sang*, p. 12.

6. Ibid., p. 22.

7. Ibid., p. 4.

8. Pierre Adolph Piorry, *De la percussion médiate et des signes obtenus à l'aide de ce nouveau moyen d'exploration dans les maladies des appareils thoraciques at abdominaux* (Paris: J.-S. Chaudé, 1828), p. 27.

9. Marey, *Physiologie médicale de la circulation du sang*, p. 17.

10. These names are cited because Marey refers to them in his papers and books.

11. Marey, *Physiologie médicale de la circulation du sang*, p. 44.

12. Jean-Baptiste-Auguste Chauveau, "Nouvelles recherches expérimentales sur les mouvements et les bruits normaux du coeur envisagés au point de vue de la physiologie médicale," *Mercure de Paris* (1856), p. 4.

13. Ibid., p. 21.

14. François Magendie, *Leçons sur les phénomènes physiques de la vie* (Paris: Ebard, 1836), vol. 1, p. 234.

15. Jean-Baptiste-Auguste Chauveau, G. Bertolus and Lucien Laroyenne, "Vitesse de la circulation dans les artères du cheval (d'après les indications d'un nouvel hémodromomètre)," *Journal de Physiologie de l'Homme et des Animaux* (Oct. 1860), pp. 695–96.

16. Johannes Müller, *Manuel de physiologie* (Paris: Baillière, 1851), vol. 2, p. 494 (book 6, sec. 1, "De la nature de l'âme en général"). Originally published in Germany as *Handbuch der Physiologie des Menschen für Vorlesungen* (Coblenz: J. Holscher, 1838–1840).

17. Jean Victor Poncelet, *Cours de mécanique appliquée aux machines* (Paris: Ecole D'Application de L'Arte du Genie, 1836); and Arthur Jules Morin, *Leçons de mécanique pratique* (Paris: Hachette, 1861).

18. All works of physics quote this: "the work done by a thermal agent in the course of a cycle can be deduced from the diagram representing the cycle." The diagram is taken from Watt.

19. Marey, *La Méthode graphique*, p. 110.

20. Marey, *Movement*, trans. Eric Pritchard (London: Heinemann, 1895), pp. 38–39.

21. Marey, *La Méthode graphique*, p. 115.

22. Marie Dominique Joseph Engramelle, *La Tonotechnie ou L'Art de nater les cylindres et tout cequi est susceptible de notage dans les instruments de concerts mécaniques* (Geneva: Minkoff Reprints, 1971), p. 12.

23. Engramelle, *La Tonotechnie*, p. 65. See also my *Rematerialiser* (Paris: Vrin, 1985), ch. 3.

24. Müller, *Physiologie*, vol. 2, p. 192.

25. See Joseph Marie de Gérando, *De l'éducation des sourds-muets de naissance* (Paris: Méquignon l'aîné, 1827).

26. Rudolf Koenig, born in Germany, naturalized French, published in 1882 *Quelques expériences d'acoustique* (Paris: A. Lahure, 1882); under his name on the title page is indicated "Doctor in Philosophy, Constructor of Acoustic Instruments." Chapter 1 is entitled "Sur l'application de la méthode graphique à l'acoustique." From 1862 he specialized in phonograms. The physicist also dealt with the speed of sound, the tuning fork, vibratory movements measured by his manometric diaphragm, and especially with "colored hearing."

27. Marey, *Du mouvement dans les fonctions de la vie* (Paris: Baillière, 1868), pp. 120–21.

28. Hermann von Helmholtz, *The Sensations of Tone as a Physiological Basis for the Theory of Music*, trans. Alexander J. Ellis (London: Longmans, Green, 1875).

29. See on this question Jacques Perriault, *Mémoires de l'ombre et du son* (Paris: Flammarion, 1981), p. 131.

30. Marey, *Movement*, p. 12.

31. Marey, *Physiology médicale de la circulation du sang*, p. 177.

32. Ibid., p. 184.

33. Marey, *Du mouvement dans les fonctions de la vie*, p. 192.

34. Ibid., p. 193.

35. Ibid., p. 199.

36. Marey, *Physiology médicale de la circulation du sang*, p. 104.

37. Marey, *Du mouvement dans les fonctions de la vie*, p. 143.

38. Ibid., p. 146.

39. Ibid., p. 455.

40. A word from the history of science; the pioneer in the area according to Marey, who always mentioned his predecessors, was William Hyde Wollaston (1809). He compared muscular sound to the sound of carriages moving about at night in London. Others would likewise examine the muscle's "tonality" rather than "tone"!

41. Marey, *Du mouvement dans les fonctions de la vie*, p. 444.

42. Hermann von Helmholtz, *Vorläufiger Bericht über die Fortpflanzungsgeschwindigkeit der Nervenreizung* (Leipzig, 1850–1852); Christoph Theodor Aeby, *Eine Neue Methode zur Bestimmung der Schädelform von Menschen und Säugethieren* (Braunschweig: G. Westermann, 1862); Gabriel Gustav Valentin, *Der Gebrauch des Spektroscopes zu physiologischen und ärtzlichen Zwecken* (Leipzig & Heidelberg: C. F. Winter, 1863); and Adolf Fick, *Lehrbuch der Anatomie und Physiologie der Sinnesorgane* (Lahr: M. Schauenburg, 1864).

43. *Du mouvement dans les fonctions de la vie*, p. 248.

44. Ibid., p. 36.

45. Marey, "La Station Physiologique de Paris," *La Nature* 11 (Sept. 8, 1883), p. 226.

46. Marey, *Movement*, p. 255.

47. Marey, *Le Vol des oiseaux* (Paris: Masson, 1890), p. 40.

48. Marey, *Du mouvement dans les fonctions de la vie*, p. 30.

49. Ibid., p. 24.

50. Marey, *La Méthode graphique*, p. 19.

The Second Adventure

1. I admit that the date is arbitrary; there is an article by Marey in the *Revue des Cours Scientifiques de la France et de l'Etranger* of March 20, 1869, entitled "Mécanisme du vol chez les insectes: Comment se fait la propulsion." While in *Annales des Sciences Naturelles*, 1869 and 1872, one finds "Expériences sur la résistance de l'air, pour servir à la physiologie du vol des oiseaux."

2. Claude Bourgelat, *Traité de la conformation extérieure du cheval, de sa beauté et de ses défauts* (Paris, 1776), *Eléments d'hippiatrie* (Lyon: Declaustre, 1750).

3. Of the three eighteenth-century adjectives Dagognet employs to describe such defects, *juché*, *huché* and *rampin*, the first and third both indicate a congenital malformation of the fetlock joint above the hoof, while the second indicates a swelling of the same through fatigue.

4. Bourgelat, *Eléments d'hippiatrie*, p. 363.

5. Charles de Boigne, *Du cheval en France* (Paris: Bohaire, 1843), p. 76.

6. Ibid., p. 84.

7. Georges Goiffon and Antoine Vincent, *Mémoire artificielle des principes relatifs à la fidèle représentation des animaux, tant en peinture qu'en sculpture* (Paris: Chez la Veuve Valat-la-Chappelle, 1779).

8. Ibid., p. 12.

9. Ibid., p. 16.

10. Ibid.

11. Ibid., p. 86.

12. Pierre Rameau, *Un Abrégé de la nouvelle méthode dans l'art d'écrire ou de tracer toutes sortes de danses de villes* (Paris: Chez l'auteur, Fbg. St.-Germain, 1725).

13. Goiffon and Vincent, *Mémoire artificielle*, p. 85.

14. Marey, *La Méthode graphique*, p. 157.

15. Marey, *Animal Mechanism*, p. 148.

16. Ibid., p. 170.

17. Ibid., p. 147.

18. Ibid., p. 181.

19. Ibid., p. 182.

20. Ibid., p. 183.

21. Ibid., p. 184.

22. Eadweard Muybridge, "Photographies instantanées des animaux en mouvement," *La Nature* 7 (March 22, 1879) (letter of February 17, 1879, sent from San Francisco), p. 246.

23. Gaston Tissandier, *Les Merveilles de la photographie* (Paris: Hachette, 1874); idem., *La Photographie en ballon* (Paris: Gauthier-Villars, 1886); and Jacques Ducom, *Les Débuts d'un amateur photographe* (Paris: A. Miche, 1894).

24. Tissandier, *Les Merveilles de la photographie*, p. 304.

25. Ibid., p. 307.

26. Gaston Tissandier, "Les Allures du cheval représentés par la photographie instantanée," *La Nature* 7 (Dec. 14, 1878), pp. 23–26.

27. Marey, "Sur les allures du cheval reproduites par la photographie instantanée" [correspondence], *La Nature* 7 (Dec. 28, 1878), p. 54.

28. Marey, *La Méthode graphique*, p. 160.

29. Jules Janssen, *Compte Rendu des Séances de l'Académie des Sciences* (July 6, 1874).

30. Jules Janssen, "Sur la constitution de la surface solaire et sur la photographie," *La Nature* 6 (Feb. 2, 1878), p. 155.

31. Marey, "La Fusil photographique," *La Nature* 10 (April 22, 1882), pp. 326–38. As far as "perfecting" the "gun" went, the barrel was lengthened or shortened to move the lens.

32. "La Vol des oiseaux," *La Nature* 11 (June 16, 1883), p. 37.

33. Bergson was intent on escaping the conundrum posed by Zeno, who decomposed "movement" into tiny pieces. However, trying too hard to avoid a problem often pushes one into another, its opposite or extreme, which oddly resembles the first. A kind of "poetic justice."

34. Marey, "La Station Physiologique," p. 278.

35. Ibid.

36. Marey, "La Locomotion dans l'eau etudiée par la photochronographie," *La Nature* 18 (Nov. 15, 1890), p. 378.

37. Marey, *Du mouvement dans les fonctions de la vie*, p. 65.

38. Marey, *La Méthode graphique*, p. 8.

39. Louis Pierre Mouillard, "The Empire of the Air: An Ornithological Essay on the Flight of Birds." In *Annual Report, 1892* (Washington, DC: Smithsonian Institution, 1893 [1881]), pp. 397–463; Otto Lilienthal, *Birdflight as the Basis of Aviation: Contribution Towards a System of Aviation*, trans. from German by A. W. Isenthal (New York: Longmans, Green, 1911 [1889]); and Alphonse Pénaud, *L'Aéronaute* (Paris, 1873). We could add to the list Alexandre Goupil, *La Locomotion aérienne* (Charleville: Pouillard, 1884) and Jean Charles de Louvrié, *L'Aéronaute* (Paris, 1876).

40. James Bell Pettigrew, *Animal Locomotion: Walking, Swimming and Flying, with a Dissertation on Aeronautics* (London: H. S. King, 1873), pp. 16–17.

41. Marey, *Animal Mechanism*, p. 211.

42. Marey, *Le Vol des oiseaux*, p. 220. A Mareyan principle: if too many difficulties are encountered, they are gotten around by working away at a simple device, as in this case (the disc).

43. Marey, *Animal Mechanism*, p. 274.

44. Giovanni Borelli, *De motu animalium* (Rome: Angeli Bernatio, 1681), translated into English as *The Flight of Birds*, trans. T. O'B. Hubbard and J. H. Ledebuer (London: The Aeronautical Society of Great Britain, 1911).

45. Marey, *Animal Mechanism*, p. 277.

46. "Hydrodynamique expérimentale," *La Nature* 21 (May 6, 1893), pp. 359–63. Similarly, "Les Mouvements de l'air étudiés par la chronophotographie," *La Nature* 29 (Sept. 7, 1901), pp. 232–34.

47. Marey, *Movement*, p. 31.

REPERCUSSIONS AND THE CULTURE INDUSTRY

1. Paul Valéry, "Introduction to the Method of Leonardo da Vinci," trans. Malcolm Cowley and James R. Lawler, in *Collected Works of Paul Valéry*, Bollingen Series 45 (Princeton: Princeton University Press, 1972), p. 34.

2. Ibid., p. 35.

3. Pierre Descargues, *Hartung* (New York: Rizzoli, 1977), adds "Art is rarely talked about in terms of the tools used; but one could write a history of art based on the use of the reed, fine or coarse brushes, the knife, and so forth."

4. Fernand Léger, *The Functions of Painting*, trans. Alexandra Anderson (New York: Viking, 1973), p. 11.

5. Octave Gréard, *Meissonier, His Life and His Art*, trans. Mary Lloyd and Florence Simmonds (New York: Armstrong, 1897), vol. 2, p. 289.

6. Ibid., vol. 1, p. 139.

7. Emile Duhousset, "Les Cires de Meissonier," *Le Magasin Pittoresque* 61 (June 15, 1893), pp. 194–96. Meissonier's hippography and work methods were widely discussed; see for example "L'Oeuvre de Meissonier et les photographes de Bingham," *Gazette des Beaux Arts* 20 (Jan. 1866), pp. 78–89; and Duhousset, "Proportions comparatives de l'homme et du cheval," *Gazette des Beaux Arts* 33 (May 1891), pp. 385–400.

8. Gustave Larroumet, *Meissonier…une Etude* (Paris: Baschet, 1895), p. 24.

9. Marey, *Movement*, pp. 205–206.

10. Ibid., p. 169.

11. Ibid., p. 172.

12. Ibid., p. 170.

13. Ibid.

14. Emile Duhousset, *Le Cheval dans la nature et dans l'art* (Paris: Laurens, 1902).

15. Ibid., p. 139.

16. For more details on this, see Charles Clément's critical biography, *Géricault* (Paris: Didier, 1868).

17. Duhousset, *Le Cheval*, p. 143. He adds: "In Géricault's time, research on the various paces of the horse was not widely known, and observation alone, no matter how acute, unaided by this theory, could not take its place."

18. Henri Savonnet, "Insights into the Life of E. J. Marey," presented at the Marey Congress, Beaune (1974), pp. 42–43 (*Memoires de la Société d'archéologie de Beaune*).

19. Marey was not content with drawing diagrams, of which there are plenty in all his books. He made bronze castings "with the lost wax process" of three dimensional models of the seagull in flight; he overtly fought against flat representation (*Le Vol des oiseaux*). This constituted the double victory over space and time that he wished for; the first was no longer truncated or reduced; while he at the same time rendered the ephemeral. This series of bronzes became part of the collection belonging to the Physiological Station; likewise "pictures of the pigeon in relief." "I have made a series of figures for the pigeon and the seagull..." (*Le Vol des oiseaux*, p. 180). These sculptures would have delighted Boccioni, the creator of the *Bottle in Space* (1912) and *Man Walking* (1913). How can an influence be denied?

20. F. T. Marinetti, "Manifesto of Futurism," in *Selected Writings*, trans. R. W. Flint & Arthur A. Coppotelli (New York: Farrar, Straus, Giroux, 1972), p. 41.

21. Albert Londe, head of of the photographic service at the Salpêtrière Hospital, *La Photographie médicale, Application aux sciences médicales at physiologiques* (Paris: Gauthier-Villars, 1893).

In the nineteenth century, from 1878 onward, laboratories of this kind spread throughout the hospital service (at Sainte-Anne, Villejuif, Hôtel Dieu, Saint-Louis Hospital, and also in Lyon, Lille and so on). In his work, Londe gave an "iconography" of the patients suffering from hysteria at Charcot; their poses when gripped with hysteria, their contractures and other forms of catalepsy.

22. See Jean Clair, *Duchamp et la photographie* (Paris: Chêne, 1977), p. 34ff.

23. Charles Cros, *Oeuvres complètes* (Paris: Gallimard, 1954), p. 529.

24. Marey, *Movement*, p. 304.

25. Ibid., pp. 123 and 125.

26. Ibid., p. 318.

27. Lucien Bull, *La Cinématographie* (Paris: Colin, 1928), p. 33.

28. Marey, *Movement*, p. 318.

29. Eugene Trutat, preface to *La Photographie animée* (Paris: Gauthier-Villars, 1899). Trutat had written a book in 1879 entitled *La Photographie appliquée à l'archéologie* (Paris: Gauthier-Villars, 1879).

30. "While I was pursuing my research I learned that my assistant who was familiar with my chronophotography had patented this device under his own name. For this to be possible he had introduced into the construction of the instrument a modification known to my laboratory but which I hadn't used" (the eccentric cam).

Georges Sadoul, *Histoire général du cinéma*, vol. 1: *L'Invention du cinéma, 1832–1897* (Paris: Denoël, 1946), p. 154. Sadoul adds this confession by Demenÿ on p. 155: "I had some well known financiers come into the laboratory where I showed them moving projections of horses, gymnasts, and living portraits. They regarded the invention as nothing but an infantile plaything...and would not advance me a thousand francs to develop it. Only later would Gaumont and his financial group buy the patents...."

31. Rosapelly, in Marey, *Physiologie Expérimentale: Travaux du laboratoire du Pr. Marey* (Paris: Masson, 1876), vol. 2, p. 109 ("Inscription of Phonetic Movements").

32. Marey, *La Méthode graphique*, p. 391.

33. H. Marichelle later published a work entitled *La Parole d'après le tracé du phonographe* [*Speech Transposed by the Phonograph*] (Paris: Delagrave, 1897), with a preface by Marey.

34. Georges Demenÿ, "Les Photographies parlantes," *La Nature* 20 (April 16, 1892), p. 315.

35. Dagognet uses the term "*arroseur arrosé*" here. Its literal meaning is of a man watering a garden and being sprayed himself. Colloquially, the phrase has come to mean trying to be too clever and having it backfire. The literal meaning is actually taken from one of the earliest French films, in which a man watering his garden has his hose stood on by someone coming up behind him. When the man looks into the end of the hose to determine why the flow of water has ceased, the other stands off the hose. The erstwhile gardener thus gets drenched. He then turns around and sprays the mischief maker. – TRANS.

36. *Bulletin de l'académie de médecine* (March 25, 1924).

37. Historians have documented these battles as well as the history of the invention.

See also Guillaume Michel Coissac, *Histoire du cinématographe de ses origines à nos jours* [*History of Cinematography from Its Origins to the Present*] (Paris: Editions du "Cinéopse," 1925), ch. 6: "Marey and Demenÿ"; Jacques Deslandes, *Histoire comparée du cinéma* (Paris: Casterman, 1966), vol. 1, part 2, ch. 3: "Marey," and ch. 5: "Le Portrait vivant, Demenÿ"; and Sadoul, *L'Invention du cinéma*, ch. 10: "Les Essais de Marey et Demenÿ entre 1889 et 1895."

We read in Coissac on p. 210, "People miss the fact that, from the time of Jacquard (1752–1834), the silk weavers of Lyon used á pierced device as a feeder. The looms of the Croix-Rousse were in a sense a model for the mechanically pulled film." It is hardly necessary, given this, to look to Edison as the source. I have argued as much elsewhere in my *Rematerialisé*.

38. Marey, *Movement*, p. 167 (in the section "Practical Applications").

39. Marey, *Physiologie expérimentale: Travaux du laboratoire du Pr. Marey* (Paris: Masson, 1875), vol. 1, art. 1: "Du moyen d'économiser le travail moteur de l'homme at des animaux."

"The motor force required to draw a carriage is less when an elastic cord is employed" (likewise blood circulates better when the arteries are supple) (p. 3).

40. Marey, *Movement*, p. 168.

41. Ibid., p. 139.

42. Ibid., p. 130.

43. Ibid., p. 144.

44. Georges Demenÿ, *Les Bases scientifiques de l'education physique* (Paris: Alcan, 1902), p. 7.

45. Ibid., p. 5.

46. In regard to industrial supremacy, France was able to keep up thanks to studies in ergonomics; Jules Amar, for example, in his *Le Moteur humain et les bases scientifiques du travail professionnel* (Paris: Dunod, 1923), with a preface by le Chatelier, devoted himself to the study of walking, jumping, running and so forth.

47. Demenÿ, *Les Bases scientifiques*, pp. 129–30.

48. For more details, see the standard work by Jacques Ulmann: *De la gymnastique aux sports modern: Histoire des doctrines de l'education physique* (Paris: Presses Universitaires de France, 1965).

49. Nowadays, professional sport is seen through the camera. The player looks at the pictures of his performance in order to improve it; a double exchange between the real and its representation; a double autotransformation.

50. Demenÿ, *Les Bases scientifiques*, p. 322.

Conclusion

1. "Les Eaux contaminées et le choléra," *Compte Rendu de l'Academie des Sciences* (Oct. 27, 1884), p. 674.

2. Ibid., p. 672.

3. Ibid., p. 679.

4. Ibid., p. 680.

5. Ibid., p. 680.

Bibliography

The following notes include only the most significant texts. I remind the reader that, in providing a framework to understand Marey's role, I have referred to a broad range of works in the text itself. As for Marey's science, my aim has been to bring out his methods and philosophy rather than attempt a complete history.

Books

Physiologie médicale de la circulation du sang, basée sur l'étude graphique des mouvements du coeur et du pouls artériel, avec application aux maladies de l'appareil circulatoire, Paris: Adrien Delahaye, 1863.

Du mouvement dans les fonctions de la vie, Paris: Baillière, 1868.

La Machine animale: Locomotion terrestre et aérienne, Paris: Masson, 1873 (*Animal Mechanism: A Treatise on Terrestrial and Aerial Locomotion*, London: Henry S. King, 1973).

Physiologie Experimentale: Travaux du laboratoire du Pr. Marey (4 vols.), Paris: Masson, 1875, 1876, 1877, 1878.

La Méthode graphique dans les sciences expérimentales et particulièrement en physiologie et en médecine, Paris: Masson, 1878.

Le Vol des oiseaux, Paris: Masson, 1890.

Le Mouvement, Paris: Masson, 1894 (*Movement*, trans. Eric Pritchard, London: Heinemann, 1895).

Articles

Marey wrote an enormous number of articles, regularly presenting his research at meetings of the Academy's concerned, and publishing them in the principal journals of the day, *La Revue Scientifique*, *La Nature* and so on. I would single out:

"Du sphygmographe," *Journal de l'Institut*, March 1860.

"Le Thermographe," *Journal de l'anatomie et de la physiologie*, 1865.

"Etudes graphiques sur la nature de la contraction musculaire," *Journal de l'anatomie*, pp. 225–42 and 403–16.

"Le Fusil photographique," *La Nature* 10, April 22, 1882.

"Analyse du mécanisme de la locomotion au moyen d'une série d'images photographiques recueillies sur une même plaque et représentant les phases successives du mouvement," *Académie des sciences*, July 3, 1882.

"La Station Physiologique de Paris," *La Nature* 11, September 8, 1883.

"Les Eaux contaminées et la choléra," *Compte Tendu de l'Academie des Sciences*, October 27, 1884.